This book may be kep

POSSIBILITIES

·

UNLIMITED

POSSIBILITIES UNLIMITED

A Scientist's Approach
to Christianity

BY

DANIEL LUZON MORRIS

with a Foreword by

KIRTLEY F. MATHER

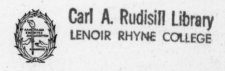

HARPER & BROTHERS, PUBLISHERS
NEW YORK

POSSIBILITIES UNLIMITED

Library of Congress catalog card number: 52-5465

CONTENTS

FOREWORD

COUNTLESS words have been outpoured, over the centuries, some spoken, some written, concerning the relations between science and religion. Again and again, the thinkers seem to have conquered all difficulties. Many times, the victory is apparently won by dividing the mind into two water-tight compartments, one for mundane, materialistic affairs, the other for divine, spiritual concepts. For each, the methods of comprehending reality and knowing the truth are wholly different. Two, unrelated worlds exist, interpenetrating, but basically separated, one from the other. Sooner or later, however, that solution refuses to stick. Our world insists upon being a *uni*verse. The barrier between the two compartments leaks like a sieve.

On other occasions, the Gordian knot has been cut by the simple device of reaffirming the precepts of ancient scholars and closing one's mind to the new vistas opened by research in recent years. Although the appeal to authority has a strong allure for many individuals, the adventurous spirit of man in the long run rebels against regimentation. Authoritarianism may temporarily prevail —in religion, philosophy and the arts, even as in politics and economics—but it never is secure. Putting new wine in old vessels is no more successful in the twentieth century than it was in the first.

The crux of the problem is of course the result of the widening spread and deepening hold of scientific habits of mind. As Dr. Morris implies, there are no limits to the outreach of the human intellect. The appeal to observable events and comprehensible experiences has so completely justified itself that it is for many the only appeal that has weight in any court. Fortunately, among those many are some of the most influential leaders amid the religious forces of our day. And unfortunately there are some scientists, highly proficient in their professions, who are unaware of the intellectual integrity and mental alertness of those particular theologians. The truth is that many "men of religion" and "men of science" are today working harmoniously together in the attempt to discover more completely the nature of the world and the destiny of man.

It is in this spirit of co-operation in the quest for truth and righteousness that Dr. Morris has written this thoughtful and stimulating book. His pages display a broad and accurate understanding of the facts and concepts of modern science. Indeed, he uses many of these in his business as a research chemist. There are also many indications of his familiarity with the thoughts of theological scholars who have made notable progress in their endeavor to interpret the Christian religion in the light of those facts and concepts. His book, however, is not a mere rehash of the work of others. It is in reality an original contribution, the result of a lot of very cogent thinking on his own part. Some of the results of that thinking are not new; others have reached the same, or very similar conclusions. The fact, however, that he has reached them independently, by painstakingly and often painfully following his own intellectual pathway across the hills and through the valleys, is readily apparent on many a page. Indeed, those conclusions seem all the more trustworthy because they have been attained by so many persons, unaware of one another, and traveling along different but converging routes.

Sooner or later, every college student runs head on into the problems discussed in this book, even as did Dr. Morris himself. Of course, not everyone enrolled in a college or university is a student, even though he wears that label. A very few are playboys, enjoying the ride at the expense of somebody else. Others are using their alleged minds merely as sponges to absorb the information fed to them by textbooks and professors. They seem to believe that the faculty has been hired to do their studying for them and that all they have to do is to memorize the right answers to the questions they can expect to be asked. Fortunately, however, the great majority of our youthful college population are earnestly and honestly trying to think for themselves, seeking not merely the skills and knowledge that will enable them to earn a living in a highly competitive world, but also a basic philosophy and a breadth of interest that will make life really worth the living.

It is inevitable that such students should be frequently perplexed by the impact of newly gained knowledge upon long cherished beliefs. It isn't easy to adjust mental patterns to new outlooks, to rebuild spiritual foundations so that they will be stable supports for the loftier and more truly functional superstructure of knowledge now available. Not only is the youthful body subject to growing pains, so also is the youthful spirit. Nor should anyone conclude that the strain and stress of intellectual and spiritual growth are confined to childhood and adolescence. Education, nowadays, is essential for adults as well as for youths. Although the problems arising from the growth of science, as its method of gaining knowledge is applied to new areas of human interest and activity, are ordinarily considered to be primarily the problems of youth, they are in fact the poignant accompaniment of all intellectual growth, regardless of age.

The two characteristics that impressed me most, as I read this manuscript, were the complete absence of bias, either for or against any particular item of Christian doctrine or scientific principle, and the keen awareness of the real nature of the problems with which it deals. Put those against the background of Dr. Morris' extraordinary intimacy with the thoughts of youth, and the value of his contribution is readily apparent. Noteworthy also are his style and vocabulary. Never for a moment is he a pedant, pontificating to the rabble; always he is one of the boys, thinking *with* his audience, rather than *for* it. Some of his pungent phrases will shock some who may read his book, but they put in the language of the college bull-session ideas that are soul-stirring, mind-stretching and inspiring. And the language of the bull-session is the modern counterpart of the language that Jesus of Nazareth used on many an occasion. Among other things, it rings true and it comes to grips with life as it is. Personally, I got a great kick out of Dr. Morris' startling achievement with words as well as with ideas. His breezy, conversational, and in places even slangy, style is a most refreshing contrast to some of the esoteric tomes I have had to read in recent years.

Style and vocabulary are important in selling ideas, but the ideas must be valuable in themselves, else the market will soon turn sour. Therefore I hasten to add that I find myself in hearty sympathy and practically complete agreement with the ideas set forth in this book concerning Christian doctrine. I'd like to make it required reading for every student who is troubled by the impact of newly acquired scientific knowledge upon his religion. I'd also recommend it strongly to every teacher of science, and every chaplain or minister, who may be called upon by such students for advice and assistance. The more widely it is read, the better will be this troubled world.

KIRTLEY F. MATHER

Cambridge, Massachusetts
January 2, 1952

Chapter 1

THE SCIENTIST

THERE are a good many strange notions going the rounds these days as to what a scientist is. While the details vary somewhat with the holder of the notion, there are a few fairly well-defined classes that scientists are fitted into. First, the scientist is a miracle man. He pulls rabbits out of hats, or hats out of rabbits, with equal ease. He can make anything out of anything else, do anything if he is given enough time, and he knows everything worth knowing. Second, he is a master craftsman. He makes the beautiful machines that do the things that need doing in our complex civilization, and he knows how they work. These two represent the Sunday Supplement Scientist.

Next, there is the scientist who is a cataloguer of facts. You find him mentioned in philosophical treatises, particularly the scientifico-philosophical ones. Sometimes he is mentioned with great respect and sometimes with misgivings. The scientific method, we are told, is the study of observable facts and their systematic classification by means of the making and testing of hypotheses in the light of all the available evidence. He is at least one step higher in the scale than the creature mentioned by some philosophers, who is merely a reader of dials.

And finally, of course, there is the scientist who is just an old crackpot. He is going out of style these days, but you sometimes meet him in a very dark alley. Obviously he is at the other end of the scale from the miracle man, and each scorns the other. He is impractical, wears thick glasses, usually has a scraggly beard, stammers when he speaks, and is always stumbling over his own feet.

All of these gentlemen wear white coats.

I

You will notice that all but the last of these descriptions talk about scientists in terms of their function; in terms of the fact that they deal with science. I'd like to go at the matter from the other side, for a starter at least, and see what kind of people they are and how their minds work. Then perhaps we can get a clearer picture of what science, or the scientific method, is.

First, I want to narrow down the field a little. The people I am going to be talking about as scientists from now on should probably be called "creative scientists," or something like that. This will leave out a good many people who are called scientific merely because they happen to work in a laboratory. For instance, I am not going to have much to say about the girl who comes into your room at the hospital, sticks a pin into your fingertip, carefully sucks a drop of blood up into a little tube, and disappears. I'm not leaving her out because I don't like her, or because I disapprove of her. On the contrary, I am exceedingly fond of her, and of all her brothers and sisters. I should be lost without her, either inside or outside of the laboratory. She is very often a much nicer person than the ones I *am* going to talk about. But the things that she does in the laboratory are determined by the creative scientists; and so are some (though by no means all) of the ideas and opinions she has. But let me add the very important point that not all the highly-reputed big-brains are creative scientists, while a good many of the lab girls are.

In discussing creative scientists I shall of course tend to idealize. The kind of man I am going to describe probably never lived on this earth. As soon as you try to talk about "scientists" or "painters" or "devout Christians," you very quickly find out that there is no such thing. Your painter turns out to be an atheist and a good tennis player; or your devout Christian swears like a trooper and hates oysters. Nobody is ever a perfect type. —Or *hardly* ever. I just want to make it clear that I know this too, before I try to describe such a type.

2

The first thing that characterizes the man we're considering is curiosity. I don't mean just curiosity about the percentages of the essential amino acids in heat-treated soybean flour; though he often thinks he ought to confine his curiosity to things like that. I mean curiosity about why three Tenth Avenue buses came along nose-to-tail this morning while he was waiting for a Meridian bus, or why that woman's hat looks funny. It can also be curiosity about "what would happen if . . ." —If an earthquake should strike right now; if I walked into church with my hat on; if I stuck two pieces of Scotch Tape together. I wonder what it would sound like if the Raman spectrum of a hydrocarbon were converted to musical tones and played on a piano.

This curiosity that I'm talking about is a childish thing. Most children are scientifically inclined to this extent. They've got to be, because they're just beginning to find out about the world they live in. Most adults, God be praised, outgrow this kind of curiosity. Those of us who don't outgrow it are likely to make a good deal of a nuisance of ourselves. If we are given scientific training we *may* learn to keep it under control, at least as far as outward appearances are concerned. I hope I shall never find out what will happen if I walk into church with my hat on; but now that the question has arisen I'll never be entirely satisfied until I find out what happened to somebody else who did. Thanks to a rather rigorous training my curiosity has now been channeled, so that I spend most of my days trying to find answers to a very small proportion of the questions that occur to me.

Notice, by the way, that I speak of questions that occur to me, not questions that I think up. The arrival of questions is a spontaneous, God-given affair. They come as easily and as unbidden to me as they do to the small boy walking down the street with his father. Neither he nor I have to think up our questions. We see something, and a "Why?" pops out.

I should say, therefore, that the first requirement for a creative scientist is curiosity, wholly catholic, quite unreasonable, and only very slightly under control. The next requirement is the willingness to try to find answers. And these answers are usually found in two steps. The first, and much the most important, is speculation. The second is experimentation, and we'll take it up a little later.

If you wonder why something happens, you usually start thinking up reasons. You wonder if the three wrong buses chased one another down the street because the city transit system is a mess, or because those particular three drivers were swapping stories at the end of the line, or if maybe it was the normal working of the laws of probability. You wonder if that woman's hat looks funny because all women's hats look funny if they're considered dispassionately, or because the woman herself looks funny, or because you are an old sourpuss. It wouldn't seem as though much speculation is possible about the percentages of the essential amino acids in soybean flour (that was one of the things, you remember, that I said a scientist thinks he *ought* to be wondering about). But as a matter of fact it is. If you know enough about amino acids to ask the question, you probably have some idea about the concentrations of these acids in wheat flour, or lean beef, or casein, and you wonder if maybe soybean flour won't be better than wheat, since the Chinese seem to get along so well on soybeans as their main source of protein.

These wonderings about possible answers are sometimes called hypotheses, though some people think that a hypothesis ought to be something more dignified than what I've been talking about. That's the word I'm going to use, anyway; and it means any idea that comes up as an answer to a question. Listen to a bunch of good scientists sitting around in the evening, well supplied with beer, and preferably with both sexes and some nonscientists represented. You will hear more half-baked ideas and explanations than any undergraduate bull-session ever produced. These people are trained at thinking up answers; it is the thing that comes easiest to them. Normally, they keep the dumber ones to themselves. But just let the inhibitions down an inch, and you begin to see what the powerhouse is that supplies that bright, well-directed beam of intellectual light streaming from the laboratory. To change the metaphor, you see the cockroaches in the kitchen, as well as the seven-course dinner that comes out of it. The cockroaches are always there. But a difference between the scientific mind and the kitchen is that in the former the cockroaches seem to be absolutely essential for proper functioning.

I scarcely need to call attention to the resemblance between the scientist as I have described him so far, and the least respectable of the popular notions about him— the Mad Scientist. I have never known any really mad scientists, but the line is often a very fine one.

3

The man I have been talking about would be of no use to himself or anybody else if he didn't have two solid anchors: the library and the laboratory.

As you progress through grammar school, high school and college you gradually acquire, often by a process of force-feeding, a fund of information. For the scientist, this information is the basis on which he may hope to make his questions and hypotheses fruitful. The training may begin with the *Book of Knowledge, Tom Swift and His Airplane* (or its modern equivalent), wanderings in the country, and a Gilbert Electric Set. More or less incidental to these there may be a sixth-grade General Science course. Later, and less incidental, come Chemistry 10,

Physics 10, Chemistry 20, Physics 20, Thermodynamics, Mechanics, Integral Calculus, Biology, Physiology, and so on and on apparently without end. If you are a scientist, most of it is fascinating, and what isn't is endured for the sake of the value you believe it will eventually have. You rely, in these years, largely on faith. Your instructors are well-meaning folk, some of them scientists themselves. All of them, you hope, are endued with the idea that all this stuff is really important if you are going to be a good scientist.

Later yet, and for the lucky few, is the work toward the master's or doctor's degree. Here you may have your first direct contact with genuine creative scientists. Some of these may be good ones, some poor, but the fact that they are on the graduate faculty of a university is some indication that they belong in this class. The amount of your classroom work begins to decrease, and its place is taken by work in the library. Instead of having to spend all your time reading summaries or interpretations of other people's accomplishments, you start reading their own descriptions of what they have done. You attend seminars where there may be discussion of work just completed, or still in progress, and where there is a chance to consider conflicting points of view. You begin to see that the things that the textbooks say aren't necessarily true. You hear famous men talking, not about truths, but about their own work, and their own opinions which are based on this work.

The most important thing that is happening, all through these years, is the accumulation of facts, the gradual acquiring of knowledge. You begin to find out what other people know, or think they know, and how they found it out. If it weren't for the small boy who is so close to the surface in us, I wonder if anyone could ever live through it. But all the time there is that eternal "Why?" and "What would happen if . . . ?" pushing you forward. It is a kind of insane thirst for knowledge, as irrational as the curiosity that underlies it. I shall probably never have any use for more than a tenth of the information that I am continually stoking in. Probably 90 per cent of the chemists, physicists, anthropologists and entomologists of the world know that the sun is 92,000,000 miles from the earth, and the moon 250,000. Less than one hundredth of one per cent of them will ever have an opportunity to use those facts in any of their laboratory work.

It is sometimes said that people like us have "broad interests." That flatters us. It would be more accurate to say that we have minds like vacuum cleaners. I have always admired Sherlock Holmes, who insisted that his mind had only a certain capacity, and so he remembered only the facts that would be of importance to him. To this extent, Sherlock Holmes really is an imaginary character. In real life—scientific real life—it is the useful facts that you forget and have to look up again. But you will never forget how to solve a quadratic equation, or the fact that there is no electric potential on the inside of a hollow body.

But the result of this indiscriminate stoking process, which goes on all through the active life of a scientist, is that there is always material on hand to be used for putting together possible answers to questions. It may not be good material, and it may not answer the questions, but it is there for the taking. Ask any good scientist a question about anything in the world, whether or not it has anything to do with his specialty. In no more than one case in a hundred will you get the answer: "I haven't the faintest idea." Because he always will have a faint idea, and will have a few faint facts to put into it, and will produce a hypothesis which may, or may not, bear a faint resemblance to truth.

Before we leave the library, there is one more point to mention. Theologians of some schools occasionally try to draw a parallel between the information that the scientist gets from his reading, and church authority. The analogy is a false one. The more reading you do in scientific fields, the more you realize that, while each worker does indeed build on what has been done before, he accepts *nothing* of what has gone before as authoritative. He must in many cases make use of other men's results, because life is too short to repeat everything that anybody else has done. But he must always keep in mind the possibility, not to say the probability, that any given result of an earlier worker is in error. And if such a result is an important part of his own structure, he *must* repeat it, or run the risk of having his own work turn out to be worthless. In order to save time we do indeed use the work of our predecessors, and we're always grateful for it. We use, right now, facts that were discovered before there was written history. But we never assume any rightness to these facts apart from our own ability to observe them again.

4

The third essential ingredient of scientific investigation—the process that follows the asking of questions and the speculation about answers to them—is the actual trying out of the answers. This is the first place where the laboratory or its equivalent is rather necessary. When you have finally sorted out one question, from the multitude that keep occurring to you, and have come up with an answer that seems somewhat likely to be true, then this answer has got to be tested, to see how good it is. A modern research laboratory is designed to provide facilities for testing ideas in some particular field.

If you haven't hung around laboratories much, or if you have formed your conception of them from movies or from the ads of pharmaceutical houses or gasoline companies, you may find a research laboratory a rather disappointing place. You may have thought of it as having white-tiled walls, impressive rows of glistening glassware and, particularly, Rube Goldberg gadgets that do complicated things. Actually, most laboratories are rather dirty. Any very active one is likely to be pretty well cluttered up, with very little table space available to work on. The glassware, instead of being bright and shiny, is usually covered with a dull gray film. In a physics or engineering laboratory the apparatus is usually both dirty and greasy to touch. A biological laboratory will smell of rats, and until DDT came along it was always swarming with cockroaches.

There is sometimes evidence of the Rube Goldberg touch, because the small boy in the scientist likes to see if he can devise complicated gadgets to do complicated things. But the making and using of these is often pretty much of a spare-time amusement, not a full-time job.

You do find complicated machines in laboratories, and they are particularly important in "routine" work. If one particular task has to be done over and over again in exactly the same way—which is the case in a laboratory testing oils, for instance—then it pays to have a machine which will do just that one job efficiently, even if the machine is rather expensive. But a research laboratory is meant to test, not oils, but ideas, and this is almost never done by repeating one complicated operation over and over again. That is why most of the apparatus in a research laboratory is of the nonspecialized type. There are a lot more flasks and beakers—just plain containers, that is—than there are meters and intricate gadgets. The man who asks a question has to be able to put together an experiment that will answer that particular question, or so he hopes. This experiment will often be not exactly like any experiment he has ever done before.

Some of Dr. Irving Langmuir's very important and very abstruse theories have been tested with equipment that he says can be bought at the ten-cent store. For one particular purpose he found that well-used oil from the crankcase of an automobile was as effective as anything you could buy or make (though, for the superscientifically inclined, he gave precise instructions as to how you could duplicate this used oil with beaker, Bunsen burner, and thermometer).

The lab is an exciting place to the man who works there, but he may have a good deal of trouble in passing his excitement along. It is hard to get somebody else all steamed up about a row of little flasks standing along the back of a bench. A tall cylinder full of coarse powder, through which something is trickling a drop at a time, may leave a visitor cold. This is natural enough, when you come to think about it. The experiment I am working on at any given moment is merely a step, and often a minor step, in the long process that started with a question and will, I hope, end with a reasonably assured answer.

Because I am naturally a little exuberant, I sometimes try to explain to visitors to my lab what will be proved by the experiment that I'm in the middle of. I always start off with great assurance, sketching succinctly and competently the problem under investigation, the possible solutions to it, and the reasons why I undertook this particular experiment. And then I get right down to the present moment. "If this comes out the way I hope it will, it will prove . . . That is, it will indicate . . . Well, actually, it may come out that way and still not prove very much. Anyway, after it comes out, then I can see what I'll have to do next."

It is when I get through a lucid explanation like that that I wonder which laboratories those miracle workers live in.

There are plenty of excellent scientists who never become good laboratory men. They have great ingenuity in devising questions and hypotheses, and wide knowledge of the literature, but when it comes to the actual putting together of apparatus, and doing the pouring, and measuring, and distilling, they bog down. If they're lucky, they land where they can afford to hire technicians to act as their hands. Otherwise they may become teachers, and good ones. But they miss the just plain fun that can be gotten out of the purely mechanical work that it takes to carry through a good experiment. There is a thrill here that is comparable, I suppose, to what a painter feels when he finds a color that gives just the effect he wants.

Anyone who hasn't been there himself will probably smile when I confess that my heart really does thump and skip beats while I am adjusting my slide rule for a comparison of two experiments that are supposed to agree.

But experimenting doesn't stop when you leave the laboratory. The laboratory is a relatively specialized place, whereas the scientist's questions are universal. The normal way to test any hypothesis is by experiment. And the normal place to experiment is where you have the equipment. A good many of the experiments that are done outside the laboratory are not considered as such, even by the experimenter. I notice on the way home from the lab that I am taking fifty-eight steps per minute. Why do I notice it? Because I wondered how many steps to the minute I was taking, and timed them. This is an experiment. Nothing hangs on the answer, but it is just as good an experiment as one that uncovers a new law of nature.

As a child, you may have walked down a paved sidewalk very carefully, trying not to step on any of the cracks. As an adult, if you grew into the twisted being called a scientist, you may find yourself walking down the same street noticing how often you step on a crack. Then, knowing how long your average stride is (determined in an earlier experiment, which every scientist has performed, I imagine), you can calculate how far apart the cracks are.

Most experiments that are done in laboratories, and

the silly ones that I have just mentioned that are done outside, have to do with material, measurable things. They are answered, eventually, by means of dial readings of one sort or another. They deal with what the philosophers like to call the material world.

But when a man's mind works in the way I have been describing in this chapter, there is no particular reason why he should limit himself to questions and experiments of this sort. A psychologist uses precisely the same kind of techniques as does a chemist in asking questions and testing the answers. His questions may deal with thoughts, emotions or desires, rather than how much, or how big. But the way they are dealt with, the framing of hypotheses and carrying out of experiments, is the same. The psychologist may have for his laboratory two chairs facing each other. Or his experiment may be a door-to-door quiz, with a whole city as the laboratory.

Of course you may say that mind, which is what a psychologist studies, is physical, too. But a statement of that sort is a hypothesis. It can be, and has been, subjected to a great deal of scientific investigation, in laboratories varying from an intricately equipped white-tiled one to a quiet conversation. But whether or not you think that psychology deals with nonphysical things, there is no reason why we should stop with the study of the mind. The experimental method is applicable wherever a man is ingenious enough to think up an experiment. If this experiment involves such techniques as love, or faith, and such materials as the composition of a painting, or the nature of the human spirit, this needn't alter the basic way of tackling it.

In this chapter I have tried to make it clear that a scientist is not simply a man who works in a laboratory, but that he is a man whose mind works in a certain way. There is no boundary that I can conceive of which limits the area in which this kind of mind can work. I hope to indicate, before I get through, that it can achieve results, and satisfactions, in fields from which it has been rather arbitrarily excluded in the past.

Chapter II

DOUBT

I

A SCIENTIST may, and generally does, ask questions about anything in the world. In the case of most of these questions there hasn't been any very violent objection from the rest of humanity. But there have been objections—noisy ones—when the questions started prying into one particular field, that of accepted truth. If a scientist wanted to know why a bird flies, or what sugars are made of, or how to cure tuberculosis, nobody minded. Sometimes, in fact, people thought that it was probably a good idea to find the answers. The rest of the time they may have thought that he was wasting his time, but there was no law against that. However, when the questions implied a doubt about something that everybody knew was true, that was something else again.

And yet a great many of the most important advances in science have come about in just this way. Someone, coming up against something that everybody knows is a fact, says to himself, "Suppose it isn't true?" This question starts off the process described in the first chapter: "If it isn't true, then what is? Well now, it might be that . . ." And we have a hypothesis, which can perhaps be tested by experiment. Of course ninety-nine out of a hundred of these questions die aborning. They are just like the question that I mentioned about the lady's hat: no good hypothesis comes to mind, or the ones that do seem too unlikely to be worth the trouble of testing. But —that hundredth one!

Chemists, in the beginning of the eighteenth century, knew that when something burned, phlogiston escaped from it. In a good many cases you could see it go, and if you got your finger in the way, the phlogiston burned you. There were some difficulties with this conception. Usually when something burned, it got lighter as the phlogiston left it. This was true with candles, and wood. But when a piece of tin burned, it got heavier. This last fact was explained by the assumption that phlogiston had negative weight—not really a very absurd assumption. Of course it made the candles more complicated; but it was found that the various gases from a burning candle were themselves heavy, and everything seemed simple again. The negative weight idea fitted in nicely with what was known about hydrogen gas. Hydrogen was almost pure phlogiston, and could be used to fill balloons with, because its negative weight would lift them. Altogether, phlogiston was a nice truth, and some of the best scientists of the time not only accepted it willingly, but defended it vigorously against attacks. Then Lavoisier suggested the outrageous possibility that there was no such thing as phlogiston. When things burned, he said, they simply combined with oxygen. This idea, with certain extensions, is the one we accept now. Phlogiston, once a fact, has become a word you have to look up in the dictionary.

In Pasteur's time, three-quarters of a century ago, it was well known that "corruptible matter" such as soup, or urine, bred worms and microorganisms if it was left around. It was obvious that these living things were generated directly by the corruptible matter. Similar processes were the source of all the lower forms of life: frogs, flies, yeasts, and so on. At times, this bothered the theologians a little, but they were able to accept it, as long as it didn't involve man. Some of the most beautiful experiments ever performed were needed to convince the scientific world that this obvious truth was false—that life must always proceed from other life. Pasteur was able eventually to keep flasks of urine either closed or open (under very ingenious conditions) for months or years with no evidence of spoilage or of spontaneous generation of living things.

A little more than a century ago a young mathematician named Lobachevski started wondering if the so-called axioms of geometry were necessarily true. One of the most obvious of these axioms dealt with parallels. It said that if you take a straight line, and a point outside of it, then you can draw one, and only one, new straight line through the point and parallel to the original line. This axiom agrees both with common sense and experiment. But Lobachevski decided to see what would happen if you threw both common sense and experiment out the window, and assumed it wasn't true. The geometry that bears his name allows of *two different* lines through that outside point, both of them parallel to the original line. (I have given some details about this assumption, and how to visualize it, in the appendix at the end of the chapter.) The strange thing about this geometry was that, if you didn't mind the first nonsensical assumption, you could go ahead with it and get a complete system of propositions. This system made perfectly good sense within itself, however different it was from the geometry you and I had in school. The angles of a triangle added up to less than 180°, and their sum varied with the size of the triangle, and there were other unfamiliar items like that. But two triangles were still congruent if they had two sides and the included angle equal; and a good many more of our familiar propositions still held.

The rest of us, even the scientists, might never have heard of Lobachevski if another brilliant mathematician, Riemann, hadn't tried another variation along the same line. Riemann assumed that you can't draw *any* parallel through that outside point: that two lines will always meet, somewhere this side of infinity. And this geometry turned out to be not only self-consistent, like Lobachevski's, but to be practical! When Einstein's ideas began to warp the physical universe, it appeared that in the great distances of astronomical space Riemann's geometry fitted the observed facts much better than your tenth-grade geometry does. One reason why this hadn't been discovered sooner was that here on earth we simply haven't long enough distances to be able to discover the errors in "common-sense" geometry. Even now, for all of us but the astronomers, Euclidean geometry is very much the handiest to use. But we now admit that we're using it because it's easy, and we make no claims for its truth.

There is a short passage in the *Book of the Damned*, by Charles Fort, which I like to read over occasionally. It is more or less a credo of his. Don't bother about his English; it is his own, and consistent within itself.

We substitute acceptance for belief.

Cells of an embryo take on different appearances in different eras.

The more firmly established, the more difficult to change.

That social organism is embryonic.

That firmly to believe is to impede development.

That only temporarily to accept is to facilitate.

The substitution of acceptance for belief is the very

core of creative science. If we take this attitude, we can consider the most unlikely hypotheses, not because we think they are true, but just in case they might be. It is of course right here that the scientist seems to differ most strikingly from the religious believer. I say "seems to." We'll see later if this apparent difference is real.

And, by the way, such ideas as the ones I have mentioned in the last few pages have almost always been opposed with the greatest violence, not by the stupid public, nor by the bigoted church, but by scientists. Pasteur got into terrific altercations about almost every one of his great discoveries. Of course the scientific world has learned better now. There is no longer opposition to a revolutionary idea.—Oh yes?—Did you happen to see the comments in the pages of the scientific journals a couple of years ago about the experiments on extrasensory perception (ESP) performed by J. B. Rhine, at Duke University?

Charles Fort's three books were devoted to an attack on orthodoxy in science. His work still stands as some of the best philosophy of science ever written, though it is certainly screwball. And he was, and is, hated with a "religious" hate by a large faction in the scientific world.

2

If this attitude of doubt that I am considering in this chapter is anything very fundamental, it should apply at every step in the scientific process. And it does. It strikes, in fact, at the very foundations of science itself.

At the very beginning of your scientific career (back in your sixth-grade General Science) you were probably told that science works by the "inductive method." I know that in my case this didn't mean a thing at the time, and I have an idea it didn't mean much to the teacher. It had something to do with the fact that you saw what happened, and based your conclusions on this. Well—what else would you do?

But induction has implications beyond this, and it seems to me that a good many scientists—at least the ones I've talked to—don't realize what these implications are. In its simplest form, the inductive method says, "This thing has happened a thousand times before, therefore it will happen this time, and always." Stated that way, it doesn't make very good sense. It certainly isn't logical. Yet it is actually the basis of all our scientific "laws." So far, every time that anyone holding on to a stone has let go of it, the stone has fallen (or tended to fall) toward the earth. Therefore, we assume that the next time someone lets go of a stone that he has been holding on to, it will tend to fall too. And we say that this falling is caused by the law of gravitation.

The fact is, of course, that this process called induction has worked very well indeed, not only in science, but in everything that anybody does. Without it, to be blunt, nothing would make sense. So we feel justified in saying that the process of induction is a legitimate one. Why? Because it has worked so well in the past. That is to say, induction is justified—by induction.

The important thing to realize is that this basic underground foundation of science itself is not, logically, a very sound foundation. But it's the only one we've got. As long as we realize just what it is we are building on, we can go ahead and erect our structures, but we can never have any rational certainty that our buildings will stand.

I have an idea that it is a tendency to forget this which causes the opposition to innovations, from within the scientific fold. We overlook one of the important parts of the inductive method: the fact that every experiment that bolsters a hypothesis is merely one more nail holding together a solid-looking structure. But one adverse experiment is a stick of dynamite, against which nothing that we have built can stand.

3

But if I may doubt truths that were accepted in the past, and if the whole basis of my methods is logically shaky, how about my results? Can I trust them?

The answer to this is an emphatic No.

Suppose I want to find the dimensions of my living room. I can do it by pacing off the room. It is six paces wide by seven long. If my average pace is about $2\frac{1}{2}$ feet, then I know that the room is about 15 x 17½ feet. These measurements are fine if I want to know how many quarts of paint to buy for the floor. But if I want to buy lumber, particularly for an expensive hardwood floor, then pacing isn't good enough, and I'll probably take a six-foot rule to it. With this I may find that the dimensions are 15'7" by just 18'. These new measurements will do beautifully for estimating the cost, and buying lumber. However, when it comes to laying the floor, I've got to do better than that. When I get ready to lay each board, I measure the length it has to fit as accurately as the rule will let me. This time I may find that the length of the room is "really" between 18' 2 3/32" and 18' 2¼", so I cut the board to the 3/32" length, and hope that my rule doesn't slip, and that I remember to saw on the right side of the line, because otherwise I'll have a nasty gap next to the wall.

I think it is obvious that each of the measurements that I have mentioned was an inaccurate one. But each was accurate enough for its purpose. In scientific work, even in what are called the "exact" sciences, you do exactly the same thing. The inaccuracy of your measurements is called the "probable error," and it is always there. In pacing the room, it was about a foot. In measuring it for lumber, it was about an inch, and in measuring each board it may have been a thirty-second of an inch, though, being the kind of carpenter I am, I would have figured my own error as nearer 3/32".

Error in science is very much like sin in religion. We wish it weren't there, and we try as hard as we can to avoid it, but we know that it is always with us, and all we can do in practice is to make it as small as possible and allow for it. It has been wisely said that even a stopped clock is right twice a day. I'll try to be wiser, and say that a stopped clock is the only one that is *ever* right, just as a dead man is the only one who is completely without sin.

In scientific work you may weigh to milligrams, or measure to microns or Ångström Units, but there will always be an error, even if it is only hundredths of a milligram, or tenths of an Ångström Unit.

4

And finally, of course, I must doubt my own competence. This doubt can take a number of forms. One of the more apparent ones is shown in the fact that I am rarely satisfied with a single experiment. All important work must be done in duplicate, at least. This eliminates certain of the errors of pure carelessness: a spilled drop, a misread figure. Then before I dare tell anybody but my wife that I have made a discovery, I must not only repeat my experiments, but vary them. Otherwise I may find (and what practicing scientist has not found) that the "discovery" was caused by a variation in the barometer, or the light from a near-by lamp, or the water that

I used, or some perfectly well-known law (well-known, it seems, to every scientist but me) that has nothing to do with my discovery.

But in all this, the assumption has been that I am a good scientist. The only trouble with that particular assumption is that scientists are people. If I am doing an experiment in duplicate, I am very much tempted to make my second reading come out to agree with the first. This temptation is so real that a perfectly routine part of scientific training consists of showing the student how to avoid it:

Jot down your first figure, and then try to forget it; don't look at it before you take your second reading. If possible, set your instrument without looking at its indicator at all. If at all convenient, don't use *exact* duplicates. When comparisons are involved (of colors, smells, etc.) let somebody else make them, or let somebody else give them to you in a "blindfold" test. Check all your calculations the next day, without reference to your earlier calculations. And so on and so on, for years.

The problem is one of emotions, which scientists aren't supposed to have. What we are supposed to be dealing with are facts. We have all found, in the laboratory or out of it, that emotions are a very poor guide to fact. It doesn't matter how pretty an equation looks on paper, or how nice a hypothesis sounds; until I have tried an experiment I've got to assume that it isn't so. And when

I have experimented, and it looks as though it *is* so, I can do the little jig that I reserve for such occasions, but then I've got to go back and do the experiment again, to see if it's really so. The little jig is fun, but it isn't science.

5

With all of the piled-up doubts that I have been talking about in this chapter, is there anything that we can be sure of in scientific work? In a sense, I think the answer is No. Every observation, every conclusion, every fact, every law, is subject to error. But in practical fact, while a scientist must realize that he can never know the exact truth about anything, yet he can continually try to get closer and closer to this exact truth, which he assumes really exists.

Everybody has played with the progression, $1 + \frac{1}{2} + \frac{1}{4} + \frac{1}{8}$, and so on. You know that the more of these fractions you add together, the closer you get to 2. If you take twenty steps, you'll miss 2 by only about a millionth, and if you take two hundred of them, the sum will differ from 2 by a fraction whose denominator would take a whole line to write.—But you still won't get to 2. This progression is a picture of how a scientist thinks of his approach to truth.

Perhaps I should say it is a picture of how a scientist *likes* to think of his approach to truth. Suppose that for the 2 of that progression, you put "Understanding of the

Universe." Then if you are a real scientist you know that we haven't even begun to form the first term of the progression yet. Moreover, the progression breaks down completely as you go on thinking about it. The advance of scientific knowledge as it really happens is not a steady resolute march to the stars. It goes something like this: One step forward, two steps sideways, fall flat on your face. Get up facing backwards, and try to see which way you were going; then repeat *da capo*.

It is in the face of this reality that we see the attitude of doubt as the most important single thing a scientist has. He must use it every time he takes a step, to see, if possible, whether the step is forward or backward.

Appendix to Chapter II (see page 35)

One way to visualize the Lobachevskian hypothesis will be given here. There are a number of ways, and this one isn't the best for mathematical purposes, but I find that it makes it clearest to me. Figure 1 represents a

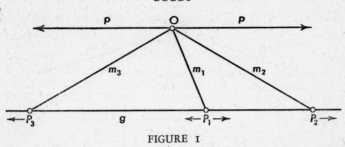

FIGURE I

Euclidean system. The line g is the line that you start with, and the point O is the point outside of it. Suppose you take a point P_1 on the line g, and connect it to O, as I have done, by a line m_1. Now let the point P_1, with its attached line, slide to the right along g. When it gets to P_2, line m_1 will swing to m_2. Keep P going to the right. As it gets farther and farther away, the line m will obviously get closer and closer to being parallel to the line g, though it will never quite make it. However (without bringing in the idea of infinity), if you think of the line p as the line that it *won't* ever quite make, I think you can see that line p is what we know as the parallel to g. Now, in the same way, start with P_1 again, only this time let it slide to the left. It will become P_3, with line m_3, and then move on out until m gets closer and closer to being parallel to g in *that* direction. Common sense (as well as mathematics) tells us that the line p that it never quite makes in that direction is the same line p that we talked about before, on the other side. And this is the only line through O that is parallel to g.

45

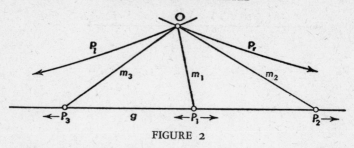

FIGURE 2

Now take Lobachevski's idea. He started with the same line and point (Figure 2), and did the same things with them. But as point P moved to the right, he said that line m, instead of coming up toward our common-sense parallel, would come closer and closer only to a line p$_r$, which sloped *down* a little from the point O. No matter how far out you pushed the moving point P, you would never quite get to that line p$_r$, and you *certainly* could never get past it. The situation is the same on the left. You start P$_1$ out to the left, and you will find (according to Lobachevski) that however far it goes, the line m never even gets to the line p$_l$. But p$_l$ slopes down from point O, to the *left*. Lobachevski called the two lines p$_r$ and p$_l$, that sloped down, the *two parallels* to line g. I have had to draw these parallels as though they were curved. But the whole point of the hypothesis is that they are straight. They are two straight lines that intersect each other at O, that go on forever, and that never meet g no matter how far they go.

Chapter III

THE SUPERNATURAL

IN WHAT I have said so far I have, I hope, laid the groundwork for what is to come. But I want to get in a word of apology and explanation at this point. From here on we are going to be concerned with theological matters. I shall probably not discuss them from the "proper" theological point of view. In fact if I did, there would be no excuse for this book; because I am not a theologian, and everything that I am going to talk about has been dealt with by theologians who know their business.

I shall speak as a scientist, with the aim of showing that there is nothing in theology that is not acceptable to a genuine scientist in some fashion—as probable truth or reasonable hypothesis. I don't mean by that that I think every scientist can agree with every theologian. Scientists don't always agree with other scientists. Likewise there is always disagreement among theologians. But the propositions and methods of theology are often surprisingly similar in nature—if not in content—to those of the physical sciences.

I

Before we can talk about any of the rest of theology, we've got to consider the *theo* part of it. Does God exist? Philosophers down through the ages have devised a great many subtle and beautiful arguments for the existence of God. I'm not going to try to deal with them all, but will stick to one or two, and try to see what their strong and weak points are from a scientific point of view.

There is one class of arguments called "teleological." In a sense these are the most obvious ones. They deal specifically with the idea that there is a purpose or plan in the universe, and they take for their material the everyday facts that are accessible to everybody. These arguments are actually an application of the inductive method, which I have already discussed, to the particular problem of God's existence.

I have said that the inductive method contains a serious logical fallacy, yet we know that it has proved amazingly fertile in its contributions to discovery and invention. We know that always in the past, when an apple has left its branch, it has fallen toward the ground. We therefore assume that this will continue to happen. It is almost inconceivable, now, that an apple, leaving its branch, should hang unmoved in the air, or shoot off into outer space. Yet, philosophically, our only reason for assuming that it will fall is that other apples always have fallen. No matter how much we dignify the facts by speaking about the "laws" of nature, what we always come back to is a great many observations in the past. These are the *only* basis on which any law can be formulated.

Now, we must admit one of two things: (a) the fact that apples continue to fall is sheer accident, subject to change without notice (and if we accept this alternative as anything but a philosophical plaything, we are not likely to be very effective scientists); or (b) there is some reality behind what we call the Law of Gravitation: the law has, in a sense, a reality that transcends the reality of the fall of any individual apple. You could also express that last thought this way: it is a fact that apples fall, a fact just as real as the apples themselves.

If we accept alternative (b), then we are beginning to talk about a universe that has some sort of ruling pattern to it. As scientists we do, in fact, speak of, and deal with, the "laws of nature." Most of us realize that our *knowledge* of these laws is always incomplete, and will always remain so.[1] Yet we could hardly work as we do to discover the laws of nature unless we accepted their existence.

[1] If one apple out of ten million, or one out of 10^{20}, on the average, fails to fall to the ground, and shoots off into space instead, that fact may not happen to have been noticed as yet. If it is true, then we shall have to modify our conception of gravitation, but we shall certainly continue to assume that there *is* a law that governs falling bodies.

If all the talk about the objectivity of science is anything but idle chatter, these laws exist independently of me, or of you. They are there for either of us to discover. If this is so, then where did the laws come from? The theologian says that the existence of the laws is evidence for the operation of an intelligence in the universe. The more you think about it, the more convincing an argument it is. Inductively, we realize that the number of laws we don't know about is much greater than the number we do. For instance, there are undoubtedly laws that govern the fact that an acorn develops into an oak tree, and a fertilized feline ovum into a kitten. We know very little about these laws. There are presumably laws that govern the eruption of novae among the stars, and we know literally nothing of these laws.

Wherever we look in the universe we find a pattern. Events are related to other events. Sometimes the patterns are clear, sometimes rather obscure. But if in every portion that we have examined so far there is such a pattern, then, scientifically, we have the right to assume that the whole business falls into one great pattern. We have no understanding of this pattern, but we have as good a right to assert that it exists as that there is a law of gravitation, or a second law of thermodynamics. In each case we are assuming that the pattern we know from past and partial experience extends in some way to the future and the whole.

All of the parts of this great over-all pattern that are accessible to us are, in some measure, intelligible. The more we learn, the more intelligible they become. The inference is, therefore, that there is an intelligence, and an infinite one, that is responsible for the whole.

In answer to this argument, it is sometimes proposed that the present state of the universe was brought about by a series of accidents. Obviously, nobody claims that each individual kitten, or star, is a separate accident. But the idea is that there was an accident which resulted, ages ago, in an accumulation of atoms (presumably produced by earlier accidents) which eventually resulted in a star. A later accident resulted in the first living cell on this star. For us, the important thing about this last accident was that the cell happened to be one that was capable of reproducing itself, without the need of another accident of the sort that first produced it. Then we have the familiar series of evolutive accidents, resulting in life, as we see it now, existing in the universe as we now know it.

The argument seems absurd to anyone who doesn't think it is true. That is usually the case with arguments. But that doesn't mean it isn't true. The people who like the Accident Theory would say that the Universal Intelligence Theory is absurd. Such an intelligence is inconceivable for us, they say. And of course they're right. Likewise, the series of accidents, considering the probabilities against, is inconceivable for us.

2

Let's leave this line of argument, and try another one. This is called the argument from the "First Cause." It is rather more strictly intellectual than the teleological argument. Here again it is important that, as scientists, we start on solid ground. If we make assumptions, we must be sure we know what they are.

In this case the assumption that we start with is that anything that happens in the world has a cause. The baseball goes over the left field fence because it was hit by Joe DiMaggio's bat. The apple hit Newton on the head because apples are subject to the law of gravitation, and Newton's head happened to be underneath at the time, due to other causes. This assumption seems to be one that practically everybody is happy to accept.[2] Nobody seriously proposes the assumption that all such events, or any such events, just happen: that it just happened that DiMaggio's bat was in the vicinity of the ball when the latter happened to reverse its direction and fly over the fence.

But if each thing that happens is caused by some earlier thing that happened, and this again was caused by something earlier still, how far back can we go? Here the theologian says that there must be some point where we stop—or rather start. There must be a first cause, other-

---

[2] However, for a discussion of a possible exception, see the appendix at the end of this chapter.

wise nothing could be happening *now*. If there is such a first cause, then it is certainly justifiable to write this Cause with a capital letter, and say that it is identical with God, the creator of the universe. To me, this is one of the most convincing arguments for God's existence. I don't see how you can get around it. Notice that the argument of "accident" can't apply here, because an accident is a cause and has causes, however unpredictable the accident may have been.

There is one argument that is advanced against the first cause idea. There is one rational way out. This is the hypothesis that things *had no beginning;* the universe has been going on forever. If this is true, then obviously there never was a first cause. Mathematicians talk about infinity, and the people who hold this "no beginning" theory say simply that past time is infinite. In that case, of course, the whole universe can have been created by a series of events, each caused by earlier events, with accidents playing their part as mentioned earlier in connection with the "plan of the universe" argument.

To me, the statement that things had no beginning is sheer nonsense. Mathematicians do, it is true, talk about infinity. They have very good fun with it, and even make very good practical use of it on occasions. But they talk about it with a discretion, a circumspection, that would shame a philosopher. From a purely scientific point of view, the idea introduces complexities of a staggering sort—you have to explain, for instance, why all the matter in the universe isn't collapsed in one spot, or else spread to infinite distances apart. I grant that an idea of this sort is entertaining to contemplate, and intelligent study of it will undoubtedly produce valuable scientific results. But the study must be intelligent.

Strangely enough, in this particular philosophical disagreement, evidence is turning up from a direction where we might least expect to see it.—From science itself. One of the theories that has been increasing in respectability for the last thirty years or so is that the whole universe is expanding at a terrific rate. By rather simple mathematics (based on exceedingly complicated mathematics) it has been calculated that, if the process has been going on in the past as it is at present, then the universe did have a beginning. According to one version of this theory, the beginning was about 4×10^9 years ago. "At the age of 10^{23} seconds, it (the universe) had a radius of 10^{-13} centimeters, and contained a single pair of elementary particles, probably neutrons." [3] Notice that if this theory is true, then the first cause argument cannot be contradicted, at least on the basis of anything we now know.

3

There are quite a number of other arguments for the

[3] H. Margenau, "Marginalia," *American Scientist,* vol. 37 (3), 424 (July, 1949).

existence of God, besides the two that I have gone over. From them other things can be deduced about God, such as that he is good, as well as an intelligent creator. But they begin to get a little abstract from here on, and to require rather elaborate foundations that would take us beyond the area that I am trying to cover.

Notice, by the way, that I have been calling them arguments, rather than proofs. I don't know how philosophers feel about it, but I am very doubtful as to whether there will ever be a perfect *proof* for the existence of God. Proof is something alien to real life and real facts. It has its proper place in mathematics where, on the basis of certain explicit assumptions, certain conclusions can be reached. But you've got to have the assumptions. You've got to start somewhere. And in real life we can never be absolutely sure of anything, so you lack this starting point. (If the theologian says, "No, you can never be sure of anything but God," that may be true, but it doesn't help at the point where we are trying to prove God's existence.) Even in mathematics, a proof is impossible unless you have *all* the pertinent facts among your assumptions. What human being is arrogant enough to think that we shall ever have available to us all the facts pertinent to the existence of God, since God, if he exists, is the creator of the universe and everything in it?

To sum up, I hope that I have shown that there are convincing arguments for the existence of a God who is the creator of the universe, and who is the intelligence behind the laws of that universe. These arguments are not, and can never be, absolute proofs. But we are looking at the matter from the point of view of a scientist, not of a philosopher. Scientists are not concerned with absolute truths and proofs, but with approaches to truth, and with partial truths that are valuable for further progress. Looked at in this way, the existence of God is actually a much more acceptable hypothesis than are any of the so-called laws on which we base our most precise calculations. As scientists, I think we are entirely justified in saying that we don't *know* that God exists. But if we do say this, then we must be careful to make the necessary next statement—that we also know nothing else, certainly not that we ourselves exist, or that there is any universe.

Contrariwise, there is nothing unscientific in saying categorically that God *does* exist, so long as we who say it are real people, and actually do say such things as, "I saw Joe Doakes yesterday," rather than, "It seems to me that I saw someone who, if my eyes were not deceiving me, resembled my idea of Joe Doakes."

4

Throughout Christian theology we are always coming across references to the human spirit. So much has been written by good philosophers about the spirit that I'm going to say just enough to show my ignorance, and then pass on.

Some scientifically trained people have insisted that the spirit doesn't exist. Some think it probably does, but are a little shamefaced about admitting it. And some think that it is as definite an entity as a one liter Pyrex Erlenmeyer flask.

A fashionable scientific point of view is that man is composed of nothing but atoms; that's all there is, there isn't any more. The idea isn't nearly as stylish now as it was twenty years ago, I think, but plenty of people still hold it. Practically everybody else in the world thinks that, in addition to whatever makes up a man's body (atoms, or flesh, bone and blood), there is something called a spirit, or sometimes a soul, which is not identical with his atoms, and is not destroyed when these revert to other combinations. According to this point of view the spirit survives in some form after the death of the body; but during life it is definitely restricted by the body.

There is some strong evidence in favor of the "atoms only" point of view. There is the fact, for instance, that when something happens to certain cells in a man's brain —when they are physically or chemically injured—the outward activity of that brain is altered. There is no question about it, certain activities that are ascribed to the spirit can be changed out of all recognition by an alteration in the physical state of the brain. One kind of injury may make me unable to move my arm. Another may set the arm to moving of itself, out of my control. This correspondence between brain areas and "spiritual" activity even extends to the realm of the emotions. If a portion of the front of my brain is cut off from the rest, there seems to be no change in my physical abilities, but the indefinable quality called initiative disappears, as well as my ability to worry. This fact has been put to beneficial use in certain cases where the worry had increased to the point where it led to insanity. People who have had the operation are "cured" of the insanity, and can return to a queer kind of normal life.

Even if you don't think that this kind of evidence proves much about the existence of a spirit, or its nonexistence, it is not to be laughed off. It is of course very convincing proof for the strict limitation of the spirit, if any, by the physical makeup of the body. I might point out, though, that just because a proof makes use of the most recent discoveries in the field of neurosurgery, that doesn't mean that it is a new proof. It has been perfectly clear, as long as men have thought about the spirit at all (and that is a very long time), that the human spirit can do nothing *of itself* so long as it is in the human body. If I see a child falling under the wheels of an automobile two hundred feet away, it doesn't make any difference how much I want, in spirit, to save that child. My spirit is limited by the fact that my arms are not two hundred feet long, or that I can't run at the speed of sound.

If I have lost my right arm, modern medicine is not

required to tell me that I cannot throw *both* arms around my sweetheart (or maybe I should say that she certainly won't like it if I do). We tend to lose sight, in the subtleties of the arguments of the psychologists, that they are telling us something we have never doubted. And what they are telling us has nothing to do with the case. As long as the body has any limiting effect on the spirit, it certainly doesn't matter whether this limiting effect comes into play at a microscopic or a macroscopic level.

In that case, why postulate any spirit at all?

When a baby sees a light, and grabs for it, that can perhaps be explained on the basis of certain purely physical hookups. Even more so when the baby starts sucking as soon as it finds its mother's teat. But most philosophers, and most other people whose efforts are directed toward clear thinking, draw a sharp line between the actions that we perform as the animals that we are physically, and those that we perform as men. When we eat because we are hungry, or copulate because we lust, these actions can perhaps be explained without reference to a spirit. But when we refrain from eating, even though we are dying of starvation, or refrain from copulation even though neither public opinion nor the other individual would condemn us, then it seems that some other explanation is needed.

I think I am safe in saying that you have been, or will be, faced at some time in your life with the problem of doing some specific thing that you believe is right even though in doing it you may suffer physical harm. It may be some spectacular action, like saving somebody's life at the risk of your own, or it may be something much less obvious, like resigning from a job rather than going along with unethical policies.

When you are faced with a situation of this sort, you can either do what is right, and face the physical consequences, or do what you know is wrong, and spare yourself those consequences at the expense of your own self-respect. This argument is not affected by which of these courses you choose. If you take the course that you know is right, but that is harmful to your physical makeup, then the *you* that takes this course can hardly be the atoms of your body. If they are capable of making a decision, it is unthinkable that they would decide against themselves. On the other hand, if you take the "easy" way out, what is the *you* that has lost its self-respect?

It is arguments of this sort—and whole libraries have been written on them—that have led the great majority of mankind to consider it obvious that there is in every man something beyond his physical constituents. For convenience I have called this something "spirit."

Most people have also considered that this spirit is immortal, though the conceptions of what this immortality involved have varied all the way from a sad and shadowy eternal dreariness to a glorious progression through ever greater and brighter fields of activity.

And this is what Christianity is all about. If there is in us no spirit capable of immortality, or if our spirit dies at the same time our body does, then there is no point in Christianity. The basic Christian assumption is that we have a spirit which is, or is capable of being, immortal.

The second half of this last assumption, immortality, is not susceptible to the same kind of argument as has been used to show the existence of God. But the arguments about God have themselves some bearing on the question. They show that there is nothing essentially unacceptable, from a scientific point of view, in the idea of at least one immortal spirit in the world—God himself. That does not prove, of course, that *our* spirits are also immortal, but it permits us to accept that hypothesis as a reasonable one, if only by analogy.

5

As we have just seen, it has been recognized for a long time that while a spirit inhabits a body, it is very definitely limited by that body. As soon as you are willing to look that fact squarely in the face it leads to some interesting new conclusions.

The spirit, if it exists, is the entity that makes the body do many of the things it does. But at the same time, while we live on this earth the only important way in which a spirit can make contact with other spirits is through its body, and through other physical things. Experiments in extrasensory perception may indicate that there is a limited, and almost subconscious, means of direct communication from one mind to another. But in the normal course of events we exchange thoughts with other spirits only through words or gestures, both of which are in themselves purely physical occurrences. This seems obvious, yet whole religions, as well as numerous philosophies, have been based on the idea that material things are in some way less real than spiritual or mental things. Most branches of Christianity have managed to steer clear of this fallacy. For Christians, spiritual matters are indeed our primary concern, but while we live on this earth it is our physical acts that determine what happens to our spirits.

Carrying the thought a little further, it is normally only through the physical world that God himself can communicate with us while we live here. In the Old Testament, you remember, God frequently talked to the prophets. We might now say that—if there was communication—it was through something like mental telepathy. Yet the only way in which these communications could be expressed understandably was by describing them as a voice from a cloud—physical vibrations in the air; or as coming through an angel who appeared in human, physical form. Even when the prophet got his instructions in a dream or vision, this vision was of something that could be seen or heard, something that was conceived of in physical terms.

People sometimes wonder why God has to stay hidden from us the way he does. If he really exists, why shouldn't he show himself to us, instead of playing this silly game of hide-and-seek? This invisibility is one rather important reason why a good many people seriously doubt God's existence. The objection is partly answered by the main bulwark of Christianity. Christians say that God *did* once show himself here on earth. But when he did it, it was as a man that he came, so the principle that we are talking about here still applies. And the underlying question remains unanswered: why doesn't God show himself to us directly, as he really is?

The question answers itself, though. God is pure spirit, and infinite in every sense of the word. Just try to think for a moment of a very limited kind of infinity. Try to think of seeing all of an infinite plane at the same time. No eye could possibly do it. But if you see only a portion of the plane, then it is not an infinite plane for you—you have limited what you are seeing. God can't be limited. You can't see a piece of him, because he doesn't come in pieces. If you are ever to see God as he really is, you must see all of him—and if you were to do that, you'd never again see anything. The sight of infinite power, beauty, wisdom and goodness, if it could possibly be conceived of as visible to the senses, would necessarily be such as to blast those senses.

But on the other hand, if the arguments that were taken up at the beginning of this chapter have any validity, God *is* visible to us in a very important way, not directly, as the spirit he is, but by means of the things he has made. He communicates with us precisely as I communicate with you—through physical things. We may not be awed by the infinite attributes of God, because they are abstract and unimaginable. But I have known very few scientists of intelligence who were not awed by the development of a baby chick in an egg, or by the sprouting of a seed. And conversely, I have known very few scientists who, if they did have any conception of what goes on in the egg or the seed, didn't believe in some kind of God.

Christ spoke of the very hairs of our heads being numbered, and said that even a sparrow couldn't fall without God knowing about it. These ideas should appeal particularly to people who are studying the complexities of hairs, or of sparrows. To scientists, hairs and sparrows are not just broad concepts, or categories, or classes. They are real things. Each one is a definite entity, separate from, and as important as, all the others. This thought, then, has precisely the meaning to a scientist that Christ apparently meant it to have.

The things of this world are not merely something that we find here; something that happens to be under our feet, or available to our hands. First of all, these things have been created as fellows of ours—they have been made, as we have been, through the wisdom of God. And, second, they are the means by which God, the pure and infinite spirit, speaks to the spirit which is in each of us.

Christianity is often described as the most materialistic of the great religions. It does not teach that the world is bad, something to be endured or scorned, but that the world is holy, placed here at the express will of God for an express purpose. We may use or misuse it while we are in it, but that use or misuse is the interaction of the living spirit of each of us with the Spirit of God himself.

This is the basis for the idea of "sacraments" as they are used in Christian churches. A sacrament is a physical thing used with spiritual intent as a means of communication with God. For most Christians, a particular piece of bread on the altar, or water used for baptism, has a significance beyond that of other bread or other water. This is not the place to go into that. But any bread and any water may be in a very simple sense a sacrament as soon as you are willing to think about it with anything but the top of your mind.

Christians who speak of actions performed "for the glory of God" carry this sacramental principle into their everyday life. We shall see later how the principle can be applied even to pain and evil. Brother Lawrence, the seventeenth-century monk, described a life based on this principle, which he called "the practice of the presence of God." The Psalmist wrote, "The heavens declare the glory of God, and the firmament showeth his handiwork." That is good poetry, good Christianity—and good science.

Appendix to Chapter III

A note on uncertainty, probability, and the First Cause argument.

The assumption that every event has a cause seems to have been brought into some doubt recently by some very important and productive work in physics leading to the idea of the "uncertainty," or in a sense, causelessness, of events below a certain subatomic size. Some physicists, if I understand them right, say in effect that if two subatomic billiard balls meet at a given angle and a given speed, their course after the collision not only can't be predicted by us, but literally bears no relation to the events before the collision. If this is really what they say, and if in the course of time it turns out that what they say is true (both being sizable ifs), this would look like a serious hole in the First Cause argument. Because we should here have uncaused events.

But let us follow the subatomic physicist a little further.

Again if I understand what he is saying, the story is that while each event is in this sense uncaused, you can properly speak of predictability when you are dealing with large numbers of these smallest particles. Although the individuals behave lawlessly, when you have masses of them you can find out how they will behave by using the theory of probability.

To me, this is one of the prettiest paradoxes in history. Notice that the physicist is saying that *these particles, insofar as they do not obey the laws of causation, obey the laws of probability.* As he goes on with his explanation you see that he insists on being taken quite literally here. He would say, for example, that if I flip a penny a thousand times, and arrange my conditions in such a way that I have absolutely no control over how the penny falls (so that the causes of its falling heads or tails are so well balanced that there is no cause why it should fall one or the other), then, and only then, will it fall heads nearly five hundred times. If, however, I flip it in such a way as to bring causation into the way it falls—if I load it in some way—then I can no longer say that it will fall heads about five hundred times. The trouble is that I shall have introduced a factor of *lawfulness* into the series of events, and so the laws about lawlessness no longer apply. These laws of lawlessness hold so well, by the way, that if I flip the coin, not a thousand, but a thousand thousand times, I can predict in how many of those thousands it will fall 497 heads and 503 tails, or 273 heads and 727 tails.

Thus, even in a region where it may seem proper to speak of uncaused events, a very real law of cause and effect still holds sway.

Chapter IV

TIME AND SPACE

THE teleological argument for the existence of God required nothing more than the application of a little common sense to the real world that we see around us. The same kind of common sense can lead to an understanding of some other concepts that are pretty much taken for granted by theologians, but are rather casually rejected by a good many scientists. Among these are prophecy, and miracles. These tend to be almost automatically classed as religious and emotional, and are then equally automatically thrown out. Yet each of them can be justified on purely rational grounds.

I

Before taking up prophecy, let's start with a somewhat more basic question—the question of whether God can know now all about things that haven't happened yet. And this question itself makes a little better sense if it is phrased quite differently: if God knows exactly what I am going to be doing tomorrow or a year from now, how can anybody talk seriously about free will? After all, if you were to accept the hypothesis that we are simply tools in God's hands, then obviously he could plan exactly how he intends to use us, and his foreknowledge might be accepted as a matter of course. But Christians, at least, do not accept this hypothesis. They hold that we humans are free agents—that we may do what God would like us to do, or if we prefer we may turn our backs on God's immediate plans for us.

The question is, then, if God is *not* just shoving us around like pieces on a chess board, how can he know exactly what we are going to be doing at some future time?

There are good answers to this question that bring in four and more dimensions. It is possible to take time, or even a series of times, as distances that can be measured in feet or miles. But I'm not even going to consider this type of solution. If you are at home in a multidimensional world, the question of prevision presents no particular problem for you. If you aren't, then an explanation that uses this approach is worthless to you.[1] So I'm going to deal with the matter by means of an analogy that doesn't need any mathematics.

[1] For people who *are* interested in this kind of explanation, the best place I know of to get it is J. H. Dunne's book, *An Experiment with Time.*

We all have something called memory. With its help I know what happened yesterday, and the day before, and last year. I haven't any idea how it works, but there's no question that it does. It works in only one direction— backwards. I remember now some of the things that I did yesterday afternoon, and I can't remember what I am going to do tomorrow afternoon. But when tomorrow afternoon is past, I *shall* know what I did then.

We have talked about God's intelligence as being supreme. But actually he wouldn't have to have a memory any better than mine to know what I did yesterday, and last year. And likewise, by the twenty-third of February next year, God will know what I shall have done on Washington's Birthday next year. Again, his memory wouldn't have to be any better than mine for that. But actually, if God exists at all, his intelligence is very different from mine; and one of the ways in which it differs is that he knows, right now, everything that he ever will know. So, if he *will* know, next February, what I shall do on Washington's Birthday, then he knows this *now*. And if my analogy is good, his knowledge of what I did yesterday, and of what I shall do tomorrow, may be precisely the same kind of knowledge, that is a sort of memory. (I'm not saying that this *is* how God's mind works, because, to be perfectly frank, he hasn't told me. But it is a way that is conceivable to me.)

But if this is possible, then the problem about free

will is no problem. Let me take an example. Yesterday I had to choose between sweeping the floor of my lab, and washing some test tubes. I washed the test tubes. Today I remember what my choice was. The fact that I remember it today certainly does not affect the choice that I made yesterday. I was free to do either; I did one and not the other; and today I know which I did.

Tomorrow that floor will still need to be swept. But I want to recrystallize some tryptophane. I'm not sure now which I'll do. Next Sunday I shall know which I did. Will next Sunday's knowledge affect my freedom tomorrow? But everything that I shall know by next Sunday is known to God right now. Why should this knowledge that *he* has limit my freedom any more than the same knowledge when I have it?

There may be other reasons for thinking that we are merely pawns under God's hand, and not free agents. But the fact that God knows what we are going to do in the future can't be one of the reasons.

The core of this argument is, of course, that innocent-looking little statement that God knows now everything that he ever will know. The statement is undoubtedly true, but it is also open to a number of misconceptions, and I think that this is as good a time as any to go into some of the misunderstandings that this sort of thing may lead to.

First of all, it may sound as though I were putting

some kind of limit to God's knowledge. Doesn't the fact that God can never learn anything new limit him in some way? If I made a statement like that about me, or about you, I would certainly be limiting us, not because you and I will know so very much in the future, but because we don't know very much now. God knows all there is to know; that is, he knows without limit, and when you say that something is without limit, you certainly aren't limiting it.

But a second misunderstanding that is raised by statements like that is that I seem to be talking as though I knew a lot about what God is, and how he works. I used to wonder where people who wrote this way got their assurance. I wondered when God had told them all about himself. But I finally found that practically all discussions of this sort were designed, not so much to tell us what God is, as to prevent us from thinking of him as he isn't.

You may show that God is all-intelligent, that he is the cause of all things, that he is every perfection without limit. You do it by means of arguments that are reasonable. But the danger is that, being human, you then try to apply limitations to the things that you have just shown to be unlimited. You think of intelligence that is limited, as mine is, by inability to look ahead. You think of beauty that might be more beautiful if it were a little different. You think of God changing his mind.

It is almost impossible to keep from thinking in this

way. What you can do, though, is to keep after yourself, only a jump or two behind yourself, correcting unreasonable ideas as fast as you dream them up. When you come right down to it, everything positive that you say about God contains implications that are false. He, the greatest positive, can be spoken of accurately only in negatives. If you say he is all-powerful, you have to think in terms of powers that you know about—strength, size, energy. It is only when you say that nothing is imposible to him that you express his power completely (though there is a fallacy hidden in the language even here, as we shall see later). You say that he is infinite beauty and infinite truth, and the discrepancies that you see in this world between truth and beauty creep into your mind. To be accurate and adequate you can only say that he is without imperfection.

What it comes down to is that you can either be accurate, and put together a series of words that convey very little meaning; or you can draw your little pictures of God, realizing while you draw them that they are false. If you do this latter, you are following the recognized scientific procedure—doing the best you can with the tools at hand, and recognizing the existence of your "probable error."

2

Now let's take up prophecy itself. Time is a slippery thing, and problems that involve time always seem to be harder to clear up than static ones. Part of the trouble is that in this real world we always do have time to deal with. Static problems are easier to handle partly because they are not real. Time never does in fact stand still and let us look at it.

In some ages prophets have been accepted as a matter of course. St. Paul spoke of prophets in the same tone of voice that you and I would use about railroad men or doctors. In his time a man could be a teacher, or a prophet, or a preacher, or what-not. We no longer accept prophets in this way. Part of the reason for this is that certain kinds of prophecy are now taken for granted, as I'll show in a minute. Other kinds are simply not believed possible at all.

In the last chapter I said that everywhere we look in nature we see patterns. Things and events in nature are all related to each other. We express a few of these patterns in the form of laws. But perhaps the word *pattern* isn't the very best one that could be used here. The trouble with it is that you may think of a pattern as being static—like the design on wallpaper, or the colors on a linoleum floor. Try thinking instead of the colors of the trees on a hillside in October. This is, at first, static. But you can't see this pattern on a familiar hillside without realizing that it was different last week, and will be entirely changed next month. In this case we can't help being aware of the dynamic pattern, of which the static one that we see now is only a part.

Now, instead of thinking of the whole hillside, take just one maple tree on it. Think about what will happen to the leaves that are now red, and the ones that are still green. Think of them dropping off, to leave the bare branches—a static pattern that can be magnificent, but so different from the leafy tree. Think of the buds living through the winter, and bursting in the spring. Think of the gold, and of the pale green, deepening as the leaves spread out.

That last paragraph isn't just bad poetry. It is good science. It describes sketchily the rhythmic events that happen every year in the life of the tree, and that are governed by laws just as definite as those that govern falling bodies. But as scientists we are likely to think of the laws of falling bodies in terms of symbols, like $\frac{1}{2}gt^2$, or in terms of a graph on a piece of paper, rather than as descriptions of events really happening one after another. We do in fact take time into account in our abstractions. But as soon as we get them written down on paper we tend to forget that time is there, and try to think statically again. However, since in our present state of knowledge we can't put on paper an equation or a graph that will describe the yearly cycle of a tree, we are forced to keep the reality of time in mind when we think about the tree.

When you force yourself to think about the real world in this way you realize that science—and all knowledge—

is concerned, not with static "relationships" that are abstract and timeless, but with patterns in which time is always an important factor.[2] This being the case, prophecy may be something rather different from what it has seemed to be. A prophet doesn't need to be a man who has a queer ability to "look ahead in time." Instead, he can be a man who understands, better than most of the rest of us, some of the complex patterns that make up the world around us.

Come back to that maple tree again. Nobody would call me a prophet if I said that I was quite sure that next month that tree would have lost its brilliantly red and yellow leaves, and that next spring its buds would split and little wet-looking leaves would unfold themselves. That obviously isn't prophecy, any more than it is prophecy to say that when I throw a ball, it will describe (approximately) a parabola in the air, and fall back to the ground.

Where are you going to draw the line, then? Is it prophecy when I say that this solution of sodium thiosulfate will remain clear until I drop in a tiny crystal, after which feathery crystals will grow and spread all through the solution? Is it prophecy when I say that a month from now a duckling will step out of this egg which, if I broke it now, would be seen to consist only of a yolk and

---

[2] For a mathematician, or a physicist dealing with relativity in any form, this idea is so obvious as to be trite. But as I said earlier, most of us are not at home with a dimensional time.

a white? Is it prophecy when the U. S. Department of Agriculture announces in April that there will be a bumper crop of wheat in June? Is it prophecy, when armies are facing each other across a border, to say that there is danger of war?

In this last case, it may seem unlikely to us of this generation that a man could predict the exact hour when war would break out. But in that case aren't we applying standards that are derived from the limited amount that we do understand—applying them to things that most of us haven't yet learned to deal with? The pattern that governs international affairs is much more complicated in our eyes than the one that governs the affairs of a maple tree. Is that any reason why we should say that there is no such pattern, or that it cannot be known?

Apply the idea of probable error to this question. When I push a book off a table, I can predict with rather small error how long it will take to hit the floor. My error can be decreased if I study the effect that air resistance, moments of inertia, and so on, have on a real falling body. Likewise I can predict within a few weeks when the maple leaves will come out in the spring. My error in this prediction can be decreased if I have learned something about weather cycles, sunspots and soil chemistry. And finally, I myself cannot predict when a cold war is likely to get hot; but I hope that our military and political leaders have a somewhat better understanding than I have of the things that have a bearing on this question.

I can perfectly well imagine a man who sees the political patterns so clearly that he can predict the outbreak of war within a few weeks, or even days.

Altogether, then, it would seem that there is no sharp line between the kind of prediction that we accept as commonplace, and the kind that seems miraculous or incredible. A prophet could be a man who was so aware of the patterns of events that it would seem almost obvious to him that certain things must happen in the future, and even at some specific time in the future.

But in saying this, I don't want to imply that a prophet would be "merely" a man whose mind works in this way. On the contrary, this kind of thinking may be very nearly the highest achievement of the human mind. The man who can do it is using the scientific method at its very best. He has succeeded in eliminating *all* of his own prejudices, preferences and preconceptions. He has recognized that only by seeing things as they are—and precisely as they are—can he see where they are tending. A prophet, far from being a vague dreamer of dreams, must be the most brutally practical of men.

3

Turning now from prophecy to something even worse in scientific eyes, we'll see what we can make of miracles.

Most theologians have decided views on this subject, and very few of them agree completely. I'd like to see if it can't be dealt with in a way that scientists can accept.

Among secular people today there are two main points of view about miracles. One is that they have never happened—that the people who have described them are mistaken. The other is that perhaps certain so-called miracles have happened, but if so they weren't really miraculous. There is some perfectly simple explanation for them.

The trouble with the first point of view, and the main support of the second, is that there is a wide borderline field. There are a great many things that are now accepted as "natural" that would have been classed as miracles in the past. For instance, most people know that stomach ulcers, and certain kinds of blindness, can be cured by what would probably have been called miracles of faith in earlier times.

I have come across two interesting examples of the "simple explanation" point of view recently in two novels dealing with the life of Christ. Both of the authors were undoubtedly devout men. Each of them described the miracle of the loaves and the fishes. One of them was simply unwilling to accept real miracles. The other, in a beautiful and subtle way, allows the reader his choice between acceptance of the miracle and explanation of it.

As the story is told in the Bible, Christ had gone out

of town with a group of people, and had been teaching them all day. By mid-afternoon everybody was getting pretty hungry, and the disciples came to Jesus and asked him what they should do. They were too far from town to be able to buy food—and we can assume that there wasn't a great deal of money available for the purpose anyway—so it looked as though there might be a good deal of discomfort before evening. Jesus asked them to check and see how much food was actually on hand. He was told that there were five loaves of bread and two fishes. He took these, blessed them, and told the disciples to pass them around. They did this, and there was plenty for everybody, with several baskets full of scraps when they were through.

In one of the novels this incident is explained by saying that the crowd didn't *really* get fed. The fishes and loaves were broken up into tiny pieces and everybody had a little bite. They were so inspired by the spiritual food they were getting that they felt well-filled. The baskets of scraps are not explained.

In the other novel an eyewitness tells the story to a Roman soldier. He mentions the fact that a good many of the people had food with them, which they were unwilling to share. But they were ashamed to eat it without sharing, considering the lessons that Jesus had just been teaching them. When the owner of the loaves and fishes offered them to Jesus, to be shared among the crowd, the rest of the people suddenly saw the light, and passed their own meager supplies around among their neighbors. Consequently, everybody was fed. If the story had stopped here, this would be a nice example of the "simple explanation" with a Christian slant. The Roman to whom the story is being told does stop here, mentally. But the eyewitness goes on with the baskets full of scraps. He knows that the miracle happened.

The first explanation says that there was no miracle. The second shows how the story could have gotten started without a miracle. But as the Gospels tell the story, the whole crowd was fed by the miraculous multiplication, in some way, of the loaves and the fishes. If you don't believe that this happened, you haven't explained anything by saying that people thought they were being fed when they weren't, or that they were being fed in some other way. Let's be honest about it. Either miracles do happen, or they don't. If they don't, then observers have been mistaken, and that's that.

But if miracles do happen, and if scientists are honest in saying that science deals with the realities of the world, then science has got to deal with miracles.

The classical definition of a miracle included the idea that it was an event that occurred through the direct intervention of God, and that it transcended the laws of nature. One serious objection to that definition now is that for the last century or so the laws of nature have been changing so fast that we don't really know, at any given moment, whether an event occurring at that moment transcends them or not.

The 1929 edition of the *Encyclopedia Britannica* suggests that some of the cures alleged to have been brought about by Jesus might now be explained on the basis of psychological healing. That is to say, by 1929 psychological healing had entered the category of Laws of Nature. But the article goes on to say that this explanation could scarcely be applied to cases where the diseases that were healed were of an organic nature. By implication, a cure of an organic disease transcended the Laws of Nature of 1929. Today, however, the magic word *psychosomatic* has entered our vocabulary, and diseases that would have been *organic* in 1929—stomach ulcers for instance— are yielding to psychological treatment.

What this comes down to is that the conception of miracles has gone through the same kind of change as has the conception of all natural events. There were times, and there are still places, where almost any phenomenon not directly caused by men was ascribed directly to God, or to a god. Thunder, lightning, rain, sunshine, winds, floods, and so on, have been regarded as results of direct, and often rather irresponsible, actions by supernatural beings. Through the centuries men have studied these everyday divine manifestations objectively, and have gradually shifted them from the realm of the supernatural into that of the natural. There has been relatively little opposition to this from the religious-minded. But perhaps because miracles occur less often, and stand farther beyond the present boundary of the known, but more especially because they are usually associated with some revered individual, the man who tries to study miracles objectively is often looked on coldly, at best.

At present, the healing of a skin affliction through the words of a wise and good man would probably not be considered miraculous. But if evidence were presented to show that a broken leg had been healed as a result of the faith and prayers of the same man, without the application of any physical force, most scientists would doubt the validity of the evidence. If it could be proved, beyond a shadow of doubt, to any given scientist that the leg had been healed in this way, then he would probably call it a miracle.

Thus, if there is any boundary between the natural and the miraculous, it is a hazy one, and it moves with the passage of time. But the absence of a sharp boundary doesn't necessarily imply that there is no real difference between two classes of events. Charles Fort somewhere points out that it may be very hard to find the boundary between plant and animal life when you consider unicellular forms of each; but it is not difficult to tell the difference between a peanut and a camel, even though both have humps, and can go for long periods of time without water.

84

I think it quite likely that events do happen whose explanations are so far beyond the limits of our present knowledge that we might as well call them miracles, and I think it might be worth while to give this class of events a little thought.

Examples in this class might be the feeding of the multitude with the loaves and the fishes; or the miracle at Cana, where Jesus turned water into particularly good wine; or the case described by Alexis Carrel, and reprinted in a recent issue of *The Reader's Digest,* where tuberculous peritonitis disappeared in a few hours under the eyes of competent physicians.

The first reaction of a scientist to a thing of this sort is to say, "It couldn't happen." And yet this is the least scientific reaction possible. Scientists are supposed to deal with facts. The first thing a scientist must do with an alleged fact is to find whether it is true. If it is true, if it *did* happen, then of course it *could*. And in that case the statement, "It couldn't, therefore it didn't," is an absurdity.

For the sake of discussion then, let's assume that all of the miracles that I have just mentioned *did* happen. In that case we have to discover, not whether they could, but how they could. We must find how things could happen that are exceptions to the immutable laws that God has laid down for the world.

And of course the answer is that they aren't exceptions. It was in 1926, as I remember it, that it was found that light is bent as it passes near the sun. Before Einstein came along, the rest of us accepted straight-line paths of light as an "immutable law." If that were so, then this bending of a ray of light near the sun would have been an exception to the law, and therefore miraculous. But the fact is that the law as we stated it was not true. Light does not travel in straight lines, and it never has.

A so-called miracle, even one that is far beyond our understanding, is in precisely the same class. If it happens, then there is a "law" which explains the happening. There is no such thing as an exception to a law of nature, because the fact that it has happened, in nature, means that it follows the laws of nature. Our trouble is that we don't know all the laws. We recognize this fact easily and willingly when a so-called miracle is in a borderline field. Why should we refuse to accept it when it passes beyond this border?

If, therefore, Jesus really did feed the five thousand with the five loaves and the two small fishes, he did it by some means as legitimate as the means by which a mother feeds her family with two cups of flour, an egg, a tablespoon of butter, a teaspoon of baking powder, a cup of milk, and a hot oven. I certainly don't know how Jesus did it. And I'm not sure that I could do it, though he said I could if I were only willing to try. But I see no reason for saying that it was something that couldn't happen in a universe ruled by natural law.

Perhaps miracles don't happen, and never have happened—though before the end of this book I shall take up the evidence pointing to the probability that at least one did. But it is certainly perfectly reasonable to say that miracles *can* happen.

Chapter V

CHRISTIANITY

I THINK that a good many honest scientists are willing to accept the idea that God exists; a God who is very intelligent, and who is perhaps good. Many scientists, moreover, would also accept the existence of a human spirit which, through a vague something called a conscience, has or can acquire the ability to distinguish between good and bad. A good many scientists, that is, "believe" in God, and think that it is proper to try to be decent people. Beyond that, they say, what more do you want?

The fact is that Christians want a lot more than that. They want us to believe, not only that God is good, in some abstract way, but that he is loving. They want us to believe that men are a pretty bad lot, so bad as to be hopeless—if it weren't for the fact that God loves the world, and every person in it, so much that he sent us his only son, so that anyone who believes in him might live forever; and that this son was sent, not to condemn mankind, but to save us. Worse than that, this "son" had to undergo a particularly painful death in order to accomplish his mission, and after he had died he came alive again.

Now, the natural reaction of anyone who hasn't either accepted these ideas since childhood, or already rejected them, is to ask, "Just why in the world *should* I accept a lot of stuff like that?"

The answer the Christian gives goes something like this: "Because, in the first place, it's true. But in the second place, if you do accept it, there are a great many things that you will be able to do which can't be done without it."

And both of these answers hit right where the scientist lives. The two things that he has shown he is most interested in are (a) truth for its own sake, and (b) practical applications of truth, or even of part-truths.

Since I'm not trying to provide a complete exposition of Christian theology in this book, but only to sketch a kind of preface to it, I am not going to try to justify very many of the details of Christian doctrine. However, there are several points in that doctrine that scientists tend to stick at, as not being scientifically acceptable. I'm going to take up a very few of these, and hope that you will take my word for it that the rest can be dealt with in the same way, or much better, and that it is worth your while to check up on some of them.

At every step of the way, whether I say so explicitly or not, what I am going to present should be considered as hypothesis, not as something you must take or leave. A few clergymen may not like me for this. But as a scientist myself, I think in terms of hypotheses, and the take-it-or-leave-it attitude always leaves me with the suspicion that the other fellow is trying to put something over on me. If Christianity is true, it shouldn't matter whether it is considered as extremely probable hypothesis or as absolute truth. To one who believes that absolute truth is something we know very little about, the hypothetical approach is much more honest.

I

Before we tackle any of the really tough problems that we are going to run into, let's get rid of some of the underbrush which tends to obscure the view of them. A good many of us have rejected the Christian hypothesis because a lot of the arguments that are put forward in its defense are no good. The number of weak and illogical arguments that have been used to "prove" Christianity is appalling. This is unfortunate. However, have you recently heard a sixth-grade general science teacher "proving" any of the laws of physics to her class? When you yourself were in the sixth grade you may have been a little bit bothered by some of the things she said, but more probably you swallowed those proofs whole, and loved them. As you look back now, some of the experiments she did for you were pretty phoney. At the time they were rather impressive, as I remember it. But . . . aren't the laws themselves just as good as they would be if her proofs had really been as good as she made you think they were?

Maybe I'm being a little hard on the poor sixth-grade teacher. Have you ever taught freshman chemistry? Didn't you yourself know that a good deal of what you were teaching your students was lies? They were lies in a good cause, perhaps. You may have told yourself that they were really half-truths, rather than lies. You believed that in most cases they would only have to be modified in order to correspond to the truth as we know it, not actually reversed. But really, the reasoning was sometimes pretty sloppy, wasn't it?

So all that I ask is that you don't condemn Christianity because something some minister said to you, or said in a sermon, was either downright false, or so badly bent that it made you want to laugh in his face. And don't say, "Oh, but this is different; the minister is supposed to know his job!" So is the sixth-grade teacher, and the freshman instructor.

Now let's get down to business.

2

The starting point of Christian teaching is that God made man in such a way that he was free. Free to do the things that God would like him to do; or even free to rebel against God. This is the particular meaning that Christians attach to the story of Adam, and "The Fall."

Some scientists like to think that this Adam story is the crowning proof of the absurdity of Christianity. Considering the knowledge that we have of evolution, and of man's relationship with the lower animals, how can anyone seriously consider that God really started things off by making the world in six days, out of nothing? And that on the last one of these days he made Adam from the dust of the earth, then made Eve from one of his ribs, and so on?

The fact is, of course, that very thoughtful men do "seriously consider" these ideas. Their considerations take a variety of forms, and not many people nowadays find it necessary to think of each of the "days" referred to in the beginning of the Book of Genesis as consisting of twenty-four hours, or one revolution of the earth around its axis; or that every word in Genesis was dictated by God, and therefore must be literally true. As a matter of fact, if for the word *day* in Genesis we substitute *period of time,* we shall get something that is considerably less rhythmical than the King James, Douay, or Knox translations of the Old Testament, but I think that almost any Christian would be willing to accept it. According to this view the world (universe) was made in a series of steps, gradually. The last of these steps was the creation of man. There is certainly no scientific difficulty there.

But as to what happened after man was made—there is plenty of room for discussion about that. Just what is meant by the fall of Adam? If God was able to make the world any way he wanted to, why in the world didn't he make man good in the first place? He could perfectly well have made Adam and Eve in such a way that they *couldn't* sin! Just what was his idea? Philosophers have argued about this as long as there have been philosophers.

Here is the Christian answer to the problem, as I understand it. When God made man, he gave him freedom of will. Man was to be free to choose whether, at each moment, he would turn toward God or toward himself. As to *why* God did this we can only guess, naturally; but our guesses can be pretty well-informed ones, considering the wealth of information obtainable—if you are a Christian—in the Old and New Testaments. There is some difference about details even among Christians, but it seems pretty clear that the reason why man was given this free will is because one of the most basic of God's qualities is his lovingness. And if the idea that man was created as God's "image" has any significance at all, then man must also be capable of love which is in some way akin to God's love. But love, in its turn, doesn't mean anything unless it can be *freely given*. And the ability to give freely implies the ability to withhold.

I hope I haven't oversimplified that to the point where it is actually wrong. But it is, in a nutshell, my understanding of the Christian tie-up between free will and love. If God really made man capable of this sort of free action, he could not then turn around and take away the freedom without contradicting himself. And God cannot do this.

Right here is another little difficulty. Philosophers are so glib when they say that God can't contradict himself. Why in the world shouldn't he? Don't they say that he is omnipotent? Doesn't that mean that he can do anything he pleases?

God is omnipotent, granted. He can do anything. But that *doesn't* mean that he can do something that is impossible by its own terms. For example, no matter how omnipotent I am in the way I can put down the numbers from one to ten on a piece of paper (and my powers are pretty considerable in that field), I cannot add three to two and get four. By the very definition of *two* and *three*, as the second and third terms in a series of discrete integers, when they are put end to end five is the only possible result. I can *say* two and three is four, or seven, until I'm blue in the face, but once I have defined the integers, and addition, then any other result than five is literally meaningless. It is only a word, not an idea.

So, if we accept the hypothesis that man has free will (and not all philosophers do accept this hypothesis), then it must mean that man is literally free, within the limitations imposed by his body, environment, and so on, to do any good or bad act that he wants to, no matter how much God might be pleased by the good, or annoyed by the bad. If God were to step in and stop him every time he started to do something annoying, then the words *free will* wouldn't mean anything. You might put it in this way: God could step in at any time, but as soon as he did, the world would cease to be the world that God created. Similarly, I could define a series of integers in which three and two made four, but it wouldn't be the same series as the one in which three and two makes five.

Adam, having been made in this way, rebelled. If you want, this is a symbolic way of saying that man has rather persistently done things that he himself has known he shouldn't do. I think we can accept that as a fact. As to whether the rest of us do it *because* Adam did (as some philosophers would have it) doesn't seem to me to be particularly significant. If you prefer—and I think I do—you can say that the rest of us do it because Adam *could*. In this sense, each of us repeats the fall; and Adam represents not only the first man, but Man.

This story of Adam is not only a recognition of the fact that man does sin. It also gives the underlying cause of the event which, if it occurred, is the central event in human history, and perhaps in all history: the Incarnation of God in Christ. God cannot "pass a miracle," and abolish sin, as we have just seen. But he can do everything in creation short of this. He can threaten and

95

wheedle; and a great deal of the Old Testament is taken up with his threats and pleas. And finally he can come down, himself, and *show* man the way out. Here we have one of the reasons for thinking of God as not only good, but loving. He is willing to take on a human body himself, in order to help us to climb out of the quicksand that the misuse of our freedom had gotten us into.

However much the different Christian sects disagree as to the exact way in which the Incarnation was to straighten man out, they all agree that this was its purpose, or part of its purpose. We had gotten so tangled up that we were completely unable, without this, to save ourselves from going straight to hell.

And now we come to the really hard part, for a scientist.

3

Everything that is specifically Christian can be learned only through other people. These other people may be your minister or Sunday school teacher, or they may be the authors of certain books in the Bible (or, worse, the people who have copied and translated these books), or they may be a rather indefinite class of people, including the "Church Fathers," and saints and theologians down through the ages to the present time, who have interpreted the material found in the four Gospels and elaborated on it.

It is right here that a great many scientists stick. Practically everything that I have taken up so far in this book can be worked out for himself by a man who can think straight, and has an open mind. He probably won't agree with all of it as I have presented it. But he can get his teeth into it, and decide for himself what he likes or dislikes, and why. Even the Adam story, though it is Biblical, can be considered as a symbolic representation of facts that are accessible to ordinary observation, or scientific experimentation.

But from here on we have to deal with facts of an entirely different kind. We are asked to believe that certain events, described in the first four books of the New Testament, actually took place. We are told that we can learn from these books, and certain others following them, not only a way of life, but a conception of the very nature of life, which would not be accessible to us without them. And finally, we are told that our acceptance of these facts is actually necessary to assure our spiritual survival.

This kind of thing seems, at first glance anyway, to be of an entirely different nature from anything that a scientist deals with in the ordinary course of events. One of the first principles of science is that no fact is considered valid unless it can be independently observed by any worker who is willing to take the trouble to observe it.

While this objection has a superficial validity, I think that it is clear that if it were carried to its logical conclusion it would rule out all history as being not valid.

And, by a simple *reductio ad absurdum,* it would rule out all knowledge about any past event, whether it happened a hundred years or five minutes ago. The fact is that we do govern our actions, and form our conceptions, on the basis of events which we believe to have happened in the past. We cannot subject history to the scientific test of repetition, because that isn't the way history works.

Remember, science is concerned primarily with things as they are, not with things as we would like to have them. The particular techniques that you will use in any scientific investigation will vary with the nature of the subject you are studying. You can't weigh an inch, even on the finest analytical balance, and you can't determine the nitrogen balance of a dog with a telescope.

We certainly have the right, and the duty, to put Christian Doctrine through the most rigid kind of scientific investigation. This investigation, though, must at every point use methods which are appropriate to the problem. What we have to investigate at the moment is whether the events described in the Gospels actually happened; and if they did, whether the interpretations of them which Christian Doctrine provides are justifiable and acceptable.

4

Whenever most of us read the Gospels with the question of their historical accuracy in mind, we find that the more we read, the more confused we get. Although they are all apparently trying to tell the same story, they actually don't agree very well. That being the case, it would seem scientifically legitimate to accept only the parts where at least three of them agree, and throw out the rest. In my opinion, this *is* legitimate. If you are examining evidence for a fact, and find disagreement in the evidence, you have a perfect right to wonder if it really is a fact.

But this doesn't mean that I'm willing to throw out most of the story that is told in the Gospels. It means that I insist on the right to look for the *facts* behind conflicts that appear there.

From this point of view, I should say that nobody is required to accept every word of the four Gospels as "gospel truth" in order to be a Christian. In fact, I think he'd be a very poor Christian if he did.

Take something as well known as the Lord's Prayer. In the Gospel according to St. Matthew (6:9–13) you find it written in this way: "Our Father who art in heaven, hallowed be thy name. Thy kingdom come, thy will be done, on earth as it is in heaven. Give us this day our daily bread; and forgive us our debts, as we also have forgiven our debtors; and lead us not into temptation, but deliver us from evil."

Then in St. Luke [1] (11:2–4), you find what is evi-

[1] In this version of the passage from St. Luke, the Revised Standard (1946) and the Douay translations agree. Strangely enough, the King James version makes St. Luke agree almost word for word with St. Matthew.

dently the same prayer: "Father, hallowed be thy name. Thy kingdom come. Give us each day our daily bread; and forgive us our sins, for we ourselves forgive everyone who is indebted to us; and lead us not into temptation."

Could any Christian say that these two accounts, if they describe the same incident, are both gospel truth in the sense that each is to be accepted as literally true? I think not. In a good many places throughout the Gospels the differences between the different accounts are much greater than this, and hence perhaps a good deal more serious. In that case shall we throw out the Gospels?

Let me diverge for a moment. Consider a scene. It needn't be a very exciting scene. Let's say a rather small dead fish, and a yellow primrose, lying on a table. Now suppose that we call in four artists, all "realists," and ask them to paint the scene. When they get through we examine each of their paintings in turn, comparing it carefully with the real little fish and flower. We agree that each is a remarkably accurate portrayal of the poor little fish and the sad little flower. We then take the four paintings to a friend—say a scientific friend—and say to him, "See these four paintings, how exactly alike they are!" If the foregoing describes anything that ever happened in real life, our friend might say, "They certainly look like pictures of the same thing, but how in the world can you say that they are *alike?* Notice that in this picture there is a yellow curlicue behind the fish's nose, whereas in this one it isn't there at all, and in this it is curved the other way. Moreover, in picture no. 1, scales 327–338 are shown as reflecting light, whereas in picture no. 3, light seems to be reflected from scales 436–557. Also, from the smell, I'd say that the man who did no. 1 used amyl acetate as a vehicle, whereas artist no. 4 used turpentine. I could analyze the pigments if you'd wait a week or two; my spectrograph is on the blink just at the moment . . ." About here, I think, we'd quietly fade out the door.

Coming back now to the Gospels, suppose we examine them, not as identical pictures, but as four pictures of the same man. Let us also remember that, if historians are anywhere nearly right, the four Gospels were written by four different people, and at four different times, all quite a long time after the events that they are describing. In other words, we haven't got the nice simple condition of four artists, all realists, but four people, all *real*. If we bear this in mind, we shall see that the four books corroborate one another rather perfectly. Where they differ, they often differ in the way the writer looked at the man about whom he was writing. There are differences in the way the light was reflected to each where he stood. There are differences in the interpretations of things he said. Bluntly, there are the differences you would expect to find in four different accounts of the same real occurrence.

I don't think it is straining a point to say that if the Gospels were not as different as they are, we might have good reason for thinking that the writers had gotten together and "faked" their stories.

Where these accounts touch events of secular history, by the way, they seem to be accurate. People like the Herods, and Pontius Pilate, lived and reigned as the Bible tells us they did. (At least there is non-Biblical evidence for this, though you can't accept that if you are doubting all history.) The lack of any great amount of secular material on Christ himself may seem strange, but this strangeness disappears when we consider what an unimportant person he was in the eyes of the authorities. Even now you wouldn't expect to find much in the papers about the leader of a small, devoted group, preaching an unspectacular doctrine (materially unspectacular) of salvation.

Of course, there is still the question, was the whole story made up out of whole cloth? Obviously, there can be no certain knowledge of this, any more than there is certain knowledge that the Battle of Gettysburg was ever really fought. But the evidence that is available, in the Gospels, in the later books of the New Testament, and in the writings of the Church Fathers from the earliest times, is at least as good history as can be had about *any* event that happened as long ago as this. While we must agree that there is a possibility that the whole Christian story is a myth, this possibility is so highly improbable that we can neglect it for all practical purposes.

5

Suppose we are willing to accept the Gospels as being genuine portraits of a real man, and rather consistent expositions of his teachings. Even so, I think that most scientifically inclined people tend to be skeptical, at the very least, as to the Resurrection. Since theologians differ among themselves in just how they interpret the facts, or even in just what they consider to be facts, I may be something less than convincing when I talk about the subject. Yet if this thing happened, it is the most important thing that has ever happened, so we've got to see whether it is credible at all.

What we are told is that after Jesus had been crucified, and was unquestionably dead, he was placed in a tomb. Later his body was found to have disappeared from the tomb. After that, for a period of some six weeks he appeared in a rather disconcerting way to a great many of the people who had known him well. These appearances were definitely not those of a ghost. This is made clear by the fact that at first the witnesses suspected that he *was* a ghost. But during this period he was seen to eat broiled fish, which (as he pointed out) ghosts seldom do. Also, when one of the disciples claimed that he just couldn't be real, Jesus insisted on being poked, so that there could be no doubt. During this period he seems to have had the power of appearing and disappearing at will, which does sound like descriptions of ghosts, yet the thing we are struck by is his solidity whenever he was seen.

Of some interest is the fact that he was changed in some way as to actual appearance, so that in almost every case, when he first turned up anywhere, he was not recognized. In fact, on the first day after the Resurrection he is supposed to have walked for a considerable distance with two of the disciples, being accepted by them as merely another wayfarer, though a very wise one. On this trip he talked with them, and even expounded the Old Testament as it applied to his own life and death. It was only when they reached their destination that they discovered who he was. Their "eyes were opened," as the story has it, when he performed the action of breaking bread, which had apparently already become deeply significant to them.

I think that is a reasonably accurate summary of the story of the Resurrection as it is given to us. We can, of course, simply accept it as being true, because the writers who described it were "inspired." We can also simply refuse to accept it at all, because it is impossible. Neither of these courses is scientifically justifiable. The third attitude is to examine the story as it is told, and see if it is at all likely, as history.

The first obvious question is, was he dead? The evidence seems pretty clear on this. The soldiers who took down the body decided not to break his legs, though that was the custom, just because they were perfectly certain that he *was* dead. The consequences of failing to kill him must have been clear to his executioners. After all, he was being executed because he had been arousing the Jews, making things most unpleasant for the orthodox party among the priests, and complicating the life of the Roman prefect. He had predicted his own resurrection, and anyone could see that if he were not killed, and then should turn up alive, his followers would have a case that you couldn't beat. Once again taking the realistic point of view, we can grant that it *might* have happened that he didn't really die on the cross, but, considering the probable skill of his executioners, and the importance of their job, the probability of this is considerably less than even the very improbable facts of the rest of the story.

Supposing then that he really died, what is the likelihood that his later appearances were imaginary? At first you might be inclined to think that this is just what we would expect. His followers were grief-stricken after the crucifixion. They must have been constantly thinking and talking about Christ and his teachings. It must have looked as though, with his death, all the things he had stood for would fall apart. What more natural than that through wishful thinking and self-delusion, any of them should have claimed to have seen him and talked to him? Then, with the years, the myth would grow as myths do, taking on detail with distance.

There is one great drawback to this explanation. As the story is told, it is the wrong story! What happened, according to these accounts, is not what wishful thinking would say happened.

The idea of survival after death is very old. Much older than Christianity. It has always been associated with immateriality. What was supposed to survive was the spirit. This is obvious, since the body always remains, to decay. And a spirit, by hypothesis, is at least a shadowy thing, if not downright immaterial and invisible. We see that the disciples expected something of this sort from the fact that they were angry or panic-stricken when the body disappeared from the tomb. The idea that immediately came to their minds was that it had been stolen. They had expected that their enemies would at least have left them this. When Christ appeared, he actually had to do a good deal of arguing to convince them that not only were they really seeing him, but that they could also touch him. The lack of recognition is also a strange item. It is almost imperative, in standard ghost-lore, that the ghost be immediately recognized by his friends, yet here we find exactly the opposite. And finally, ghosts may rattle spectral chains, but they never have been known to eat real food. Notice, by the way, that although he ate, he didn't drink wine. Thus there was something very selective about the way he was able, or willing, to take nourishment. This is a very minor point, but it doesn't sound like the kind of thing that you would make up.

All of this just doesn't fit with an invented story, even one invented with the best of will. I rather think that if I had been one of his followers, I might have found it quite credible that he had turned up on occasions, and had been seen by one or several people; perhaps confronted Pilate—that would have been a nice touch—and scared the soldiers who had executed him. All kinds of exciting, and convincing, stories might have gone the rounds. But the very improbability of the story that is actually told is a rather important piece of evidence in its favor.

There is one more line of argument, on which historians nowadays are laying more and more stress. This is the purely psychological one of the effect of the resurrection on the characters of the disciples. As you read the accounts of the crucifixion you find that Christ himself knew just what he was facing, and had tried to prepare the disciples for it. But when it came to the point, the disciples couldn't take it. He asked them to watch while he prayed in the garden of Gethsemane. They seem not to have taken the danger seriously, and to have fallen asleep at their posts. When the High Priest's men came to capture him, the disciples panicked. Peter, it is true, swung with a sword, but he missed, and only cut off his opponent's ear.

Later, Peter managed to sneak into the courtyard where the prisoner was being held, but when he was accused of being in league with the troublemakers he denied it time and again, swearing that he didn't even know Jesus. It appears that at the scene of the crucifixion Jesus' mother, Mary, and the other Mary, were there. But John was the only one of the disciples who dared take the risk of being seen and known as one of the partisans of the new movement, now apparently defeated.

Then, only a few weeks later, there is a complete change. Peter, the coward who had vociferously insisted in the courtyard that *he* was no Christian, faces the very same people who had executed his master, and accuses them of their crime. He and the other disciples go out through the country boasting of their association with the man whose cause had seemed lost.

They certainly knew the danger they were in. Peter was soon shut up in jail overnight, though on this occasion he was released because the general population of Jerusalem had begun to be somewhat sympathetic to the Christians. But before long Stephen, one of the new disciples, was stoned to death after a particularly courageous speech to the High Priest and his supporters. Here, and from here on, we find in all of the Christians a completely reckless disregard for their own safety.

The point I am trying to make is that something tremendous must have happened to this group of men, who had been hopeless and even cowardly, to make them capable of taking a course of action that was completely selfless and terribly dangerous. The explanation that Christianity gives for the change is the Resurrection. That explanation is certainly adequate. True, you could think of other explanations. That isn't the point. History consists of what *did* happen, not of the much nicer things that might have happened.

I am under no illusion that I have "proved" the actuality of the Resurrection, or even made it credible. I have an idea that this is one point in Christian doctrine (and there are others) that cannot be made, strictly speaking, credible. As with Lobachevski's hypothesis, you must decide first whether it seems to be self-consistent. Then, like Riemann's, it may turn out to be valid. A great many people have lived on the assumption that it is. Their lives are part of the evidence that must be collected and examined to see if the hypothesis fits with reality.

Christians tell me that at a certain point, in that process of collecting evidence, something happens. From then on you believe that the Christian teachings are not merely a probable hypothesis, but true. I have not yet reached that point. Later on, I plan to take up this question of Faith. But for the moment we shall have to leave the question of the Resurrection as one of the tenets of Christianity which is, by its very nature, so remote from anything we meet in our ordinary thinking that there is nothing we can compare it with.

I want to end this chapter with a paragraph from the book, *The Gospel and Modern Thought,* by Alan Richardson.

Our inquiry has led us to see that the Christian Church is historically the result of a certain historical event or series of events. That is to say, Christianity is not based upon any theory which philosophers or theologians have worked out for themselves; it is not the result of the brilliant discovery of a new idea about God; the Christian Church did not come into existence because someone had enunciated the view that God is love, or that mankind are brethren. All such ideas had been familiar to the Jews for a very long time. If Jesus had merely been a teacher of such truths, no Church would have come into existence and we would never even have heard of his name. The Church can be understood only as the outcome of those very events which the New Testament records and which the Church still exists to proclaim. That is why the Apostles' Creed, the ancient baptismal creed of Christendom, is concerned not with ideas about God, but with statements of historical facts: ". . . suffered under Pontius Pilate, was crucified, dead and buried, he descended into hell; the third day he rose again from the dead. . . ." That is why, also, the Christian preaching does not start with the affirmation of ideas or the commendation of theories; it has always been, since the days of the apostles themselves, a preaching of the cross and resurrection of Jesus. It has always been the handing on of a testimony, the telling of news, the bearing of witness. It is a proclamation of what has happened, not of what men have thought or felt or wished. If the fact is established, the theory and ideas will look after themselves. If Jesus rose from the dead, then our views about the universe and life must be adjusted to take account of this fact. If this is the kind of universe in which such an event as the resurrection of Jesus actually did happen, what sort of universe must it be? What kind of purpose must it have? What kind of philosophy do we need to explain it? A Christian philosophy will be a view of the universe which discovers its meaning in this central fact of the resurrection of Jesus.

Chapter VI

CHRISTIAN BEHAVIOR

IN THE beginning of the last chapter I said that it might be argued that Christianity is important to a scientist first because it's true, and second because of what can be done with it. It is the second half of this that I want to deal with now. I am not going to try to take up the whole question of Christian behavior, any more than I tried to give any significant fraction of Christian doctrine in the last chapter. Instead, I'm going to consider just one aspect of it—though I think everybody will agree that it is the most important single aspect.

I

When somebody asked Christ which were the greatest of the commandments, the bystanders probably expected that some of the great ten would be cited. Instead, Christ quoted two that were apparently not very well known, though they can be found in the Old Testament. These were, "Thou shalt love the Lord thy God with all thy heart and with all thy soul and with all thy mind"; and "Thou shalt love thy neighbor as thyself." He then went on to say that all of the law, and the teachings of the prophets, depend on these two commandments; that is to say, they sum up all the moral teachings of the Old Testament.

If anyone else had quoted these commandments, they might have had relatively little meaning. History is full of nice neat moral precepts, a good many of them at least as pretty as these, and some with more apparent value. We recall them from time to time—quotes like the Greek "Know thyself," Shakespeare's "To thine own self be true," or Ben Franklin's questionable "Honesty is the best policy"—and think that we probably ought to try to live by them, or would if we had more time.

But the Great Commandments have taken on an importance that seems to be out of proportion to the words themselves. In fact, it is an importance that is almost unrelated to the words. Any semanticist will tell you that they have really very little meaning of any sort. And any Christian, after due thought, will perhaps be forced to agree. What makes the commandments important is the *interpretation* of them which was furnished by Christ himself, not only in words, but in his whole life. This interpretation was so clear and explicit that his disciples had no difficulty in knowing how to follow the commandments after his death, and Christians have used them intelligently (or at least known how to) ever since.

During the century just passed, however, there grew up a queer perversion of Christianity, that associated it with a kind of wishy-washiness. To be a Christian you should wear frumpy clothes and a pious look, never speak above a whisper, and above all never give offense to anybody. I think this may explain the disrepute that "Christian love" has fallen into. If, to be a Christian, you had to go around saying how pretty those slums were, and what a lovely boy that murderer was at heart, honest people often felt justified in saying "To hell with it!"

2

But as Christ interpreted the idea in his teachings and actions and as the apostles used it throughout their lives, love of your neighbor (which is what I'm going to deal with specifically) is a great deal more than a pleasant emotion. In fact, as we study it we see that it can only be described by some word like *technique* or *method,* and that the emotions that accompany it are often decidedly unpleasant ones. It frequently involves a conscious putting aside of my own immediate desires, or even of my own welfare. And it requires a kind of objectivity that is, at first sight anyway, very different from the *emotion* called love.

Perhaps it was for reasons like this that the older

English translators sometimes used the word *charity* instead of *love,* and some contemporary Catholic writers are taking to the frank use of the Latin *caritas.* The trouble with *charity* is that it now has a meaning that is entirely different from the kind of love that we are talking about. It is worth mentioning that the problem of how to translate the word is not a modern one. In the fifth century, St. Augustine discussed the Latin words for love which should be used to translate the several *Greek* words for it in the New Testament.

I suggested that Christian love might be considered as a technique. If so, it bears very little relationship to the technique involved in handling an analytical balance, or in doing a fractional distillation. But in scientific work there are other techniques, that I may have hinted at in my chapter on doubt, that are much more subtle than these, and no less important. I'm going to take a minute to go into two of them.

A good scientist differs from a bad one not only by how well he handles his instruments, but by how he deals with his results when he gets them. As we progress through our training in science we gradually learn to know what is good evidence for believing that something is true. Any veteran teacher will recognize the fact that this ability doesn't "come naturally" to the majority of students; but it can be taught. There is no one accepted name for it, but it is often called intellectual honesty.

Its possessor has learned the difficult art of criticizing his own work, instead of having to have it criticized by other people. He waits to announce a result until the evidence is more than convincing, instead of shooting off his face at the first hopeful-looking experiment. When he lectures, he gives you the feeling that he knows what he is talking about. It is almost impossible to give an explicit description of intellectual honesty, but if you have it, or know people who have it, you know that it is something real and definite.

Another of these subtle techniques that make a man a good scientist is an equally undefinable one called *serendipity*. You will find this word in any big dictionary. It was coined by Horace Walpole, and comes from an old fairy tale about the three princes of Serendip who went out in search of what they weren't looking for. Dr. Walter B. Cannon, the famous physiologist, brought the word back into use, because it so perfectly describes something that a good scientist must have.

I'm not sure that serendipity can be taught, but I think it can, if only by example. You might ascribe to it the discovery of penicillin, for instance, or of radium, or of the laws of gravitation. A man is working in his laboratory or sitting under an apple tree, when an accident happens. His experiment fails, or he gets hit on the head by an apple. Things like this happen to most people fairly often. The scientist who has learned the art of serendipity starts thinking in an entirely new direction, and (one time out of a thousand) a discovery results. Scientists are usually pretty modest about this sort of thing. They often shrug it off as sheer accident. Yet the accidents happen to everybody; the best of the trained scientists have learned the technique of using them.

You probably see what I am getting at, now. *Love,* as it appears in Christian teachings, is just as definitely a technique as the ones I have been talking about. It may be true that this kind of love has very little to do with success in the laboratory (though the point could be argued). But as I said earlier, the laboratory is only a part, and often a small part, of the stage on which the scientist plays his role. We actually do use our scientific methods throughout the rest of our activities, from shopping trips to churchgoing. A queer, reverse-English demonstration of this is the very fact that scientists sometimes reject Christianity because it is "not scientific." That is, we do expect to use science outside of the laboratory, and are disappointed if it doesn't seem to be applicable.

Christians say that love will accomplish things that can be done in no other way. And we must admit that the evidence, looked at objectively, is strong. Unquestionably the Hitlers, Napoleons, and Neros of this world have had profound effects on it, showing that hate and pride are also powerful agents. But the things that have been done by people like Lincoln and Gandhi, St. Francis of Assisi and Bernadotte of Sweden, could not have been accomplished without the love, of the Christian type, that was used in doing them. This was no vague "well-feeling" toward their fellow men, but a positive, active *method;* a mode of action by which apparently unsurmountable obstacles were overcome.

3

If this Christian love that I am talking about is so different from what people ordinarily mean by love, why use the word at all? How did two such very different ideas get confused? I think that perhaps by answering this question, I can at the same time make a start at defining Christian love. Because when you step up the ordinary kind of love to its highest level—when you apply just the opposite of a *reductio ad absurdum* to it—then you get Christian love.

When a boy and girl fall in love, this is usually caused by the desire of each for the love of the other. The relationship starts with emotions which may be primarily selfish. Each wants to *get* something: fun, appreciation, excitement, beauty; and of course eventually sexual satisfaction. None of these at the start can properly be identified with the method or technique that we're talking about here. However, notice that whenever the boy or girl *gets* one of the things he wants, the other must *give* it, so that almost at once, in a normal boy-girl affair, love in the Christian sense enters the picture. While each still wants in a (perfectly legitimately) selfish way to have his needs met, at the same time each is trying (if only for selfish reasons at first) to meet the needs of the other. The moment this happens, the technique becomes that of Christian love. The girl has beauty to offer: she takes more trouble to make herself beautiful in his eyes. The boy exerts all the charm he has, puts his skill and strength in her service in every way he can think of, even if at the start it is only to carry her books. Each laughs at the other's jokes, jokes that may sound terribly feeble to an outsider. It is just a question of time before a good many of the original selfish emotions have simply evaporated.

I don't think I'm idealizing much here. Suppose you think back to the time when you were first in love. After the first shock had worn off, didn't you find yourself doing things that you would have considered foolish, or beneath you, only a few weeks earlier? If a boy, weren't you putting up with "girl stuff" that you had been laughing at in other boys? If a girl, weren't you finding charming the clumsy antics that had disgusted you?

Not only that, but as an adult have you noticed the change that comes over both the boy and girl, not only in the way they behave toward each other, but toward the rest of the world? The boy, when he notices the satisfaction to himself in being polite and friendly to the girl, tries it at home for a change. The girl may *offer* to do the dishes, instead of having to be driven. The two of them have suddenly discovered that "doing things for people" isn't just something that teachers have told them is their moral duty, but that it is fun.

There is a little poem in Housman's *A Shropshire Lad* that illustrates the point, both in the direct and the inverted sense:

> Oh, when I was in love with you,
>   Then I was clean and brave.
> And miles around the wonder grew
>   How well did I behave.
>
> And now the fancy passes by,
>   And nothing will remain,
> And all around they'll say that I
>   Am quite myself again.[1]

As sexual love ripens it may become more, or less, Christian. If more, then it often develops into the "ideal" marriages, where the couple are so used to selfless action toward each other that it becomes a habit. These are the people who are still "in love" twenty and fifty years later, and who are a joy to their family and friends. Or the selfish aspects may predominate, so that each gives only what is required, as a bargain, to get what he wants.

[1] Reprinted with permission of Henry Holt and Company, Inc., The Society of Authors, London, and Messrs. Jonathan Cape, Ltd.

Unfortunately, there are enough of these so that I don't have to describe them further.

Another common use of the word *love* applies to the relationship between parent and child. Here, by the nature of the case, it is Christian love that is present at the very start. The child can give nothing. It is helpless. The parent is in the position of giving everything, and expecting nothing in return. Obviously there are exceptions, but in most cases, at first anyway, the parents are using all the methods of Christian love toward the child. They will put up with terrific indignities, make unbelievable sacrifices, for the welfare of the child. Notice, by the way, that a truly loving parent is motivated so exclusively by the welfare of the child that he or she is willing that the child should suffer considerable discomfort or pain on occasions, if this will prevent future suffering. The spoiled child is likely to be the offspring of selfish, not of loving parents. They use the "this hurts me more than it does you" as an excuse for not hurting themselves.

It seems likely that the nature of this parent-child relationship is in part responsible for the Biblical metaphor of God as the Father. Since God himself is the supreme example of love in its highest sense, and the love of a parent for a child is the closest thing there is in nature to selfless love, then this is the best metaphor that could possibly be used. God has given us everything we have. We have nothing to give him that he needs. He may punish his people, but he does it in a parental way, to make them better; to make them eventually more capable of loving as he loves.

You can go on for yourself with examples of this sort. Christian love is by no means absent from the kind of love we usually talk about, but it has very little to do with the emotion called love. Christians tell us that it is possible, and in fact necessary, to love people whom you dislike thoroughly. Christ said, "Love your enemies." There is no implication here that we should *like* our enemies; in fact, if we did they probably wouldn't be our enemies. It is said that St. Francis of Assisi, early in his career, had a fear and hatred of leprosy. It was a "physical repulsion"—a deep emotional revulsion. The story is told that on one occasion he was riding horseback, and passed a leper on the road. He reined his horse to the side, giving the man as wide a berth as possible, and rode on. Then suddenly he turned back, sprang from his horse and, throwing his arms around the leper, kissed him on his diseased face. Notice that the *emotions* involved here are fear, hatred, revulsion. The *action* is love.

4

I seem to have been trying to say what Christian love is by means of a series of analogies. Maybe that's the best way to do it. How would you instruct somebody, in words, on how to be intellectually honest, or how to use serendipity? Yet I should like to bring in one or two points that haven't specifically appeared as yet.

For one thing there is the idea that being Christian meant being a doormat, an idea that seems to have made its appearance during the last century. Somebody who interprets love as never getting into a fight still has a lot to learn. Likewise the man who spoke of "Gentle Jesus, meek and mild" can't have read his Bible with any great understanding. Christ did indeed teach that we should submit meekly to insults and injustices *to ourselves*. He did not fight when he was captured, spat on, beaten, and finally, after a mock-trial, executed. But remember what happened when he found the money-changers in his Father's house. The picture that we have is of a thoroughly angry man. There was no gentleness in the way he overturned tables, whipped the desecraters with a real whip that was swung to hurt, and generally "broke up the joint." This was no doormat.

Christ's whole ministry was a running battle with the orthodox priests. There is no sign anywhere of his giving way on a matter of principle. Some Christians would have it that the story of the whipping of the money-changers is apocryphal, that this incident is not in character with the Christ who is portrayed in the rest of the Gospels. It is true that this is the only occasion where he is shown as using physical violence. But anyone who has had any experience with academic life knows that the emotions that are aroused in the course of a debate on a genuine matter of right and wrong are often much more violent than those of a rough-and-tumble fight. In each of the Gospels we read about debate of the bitterest sort, with Jesus lashing out in words as unrestrainedly—and as effectively—as he did with his whip in the temple. The incident is certainly in character.

No; Christian love can't always be gentle. But at the same time, when it is violent it must always be made clear that the violence is not personal. If a father spanks his son because daddy's feelings are hurt, there is no love there. But a father may spank his son because the boy has done wrong and this is the only way to prevent his doing it again. It may tear daddy's heart, but he does it because he loves the boy. This last example may well be as close as we can get to an idea of necessary Christian violence. When a perfect father-son relationship exists, such a spanking is completely in keeping with the relationship.

Great subtlety may be required in the exercise of love as a technique. A beautiful example of this was the occasion in Jerusalem when a woman had been caught in adultery. The old bitter Jewish law required, or at least permitted, that she be taken outside the city and stoned to death. Here was a case where the orthodox party were certain that they were acting within their rights. They challenged Jesus with it, knowing that he must inevitably show himself as outside the law if he interfered with the execution. The picture that we are given is of the crowd standing close around him, and we can imagine the deep silence while they waited to see how he could possibly deal with this impossible situation. Jesus is described as doodling in the sand—drawing pictures with his finger. Suddenly he stands up, and quietly says, "You're right. That is the law. Suppose you just have the man among you who hasn't sinned throw the first stone." Then he stoops again and resumes his doodling in the sand. We are told that the crowd literally melted away; Jesus didn't even look up again until they had gone. Then he turned to the woman and told her to go—and not to sin again. Here was a case where loud words could not have done what needed doing; where nothing could have been accomplished by philosophical debate. It was a case of the application of sheer, cold-blooded Christian love.

I know that those look like funny words—cold-blooded love. Yet I think they are properly used. This technique is not the vague beneficence that is implied by the expression "a way of life." It isn't something that is accompanied by floating scarves for women, or lack of haircuts for men. It is a deliberate, cultivated technique. Anyone from a moron on up can apply it, but the more clear, cold, calculating thought that can be applied to it, the more effective it can be. It has been very well said that Christ was the only man that ever lived who was shrewder than the very Devil.

As we have just seen, love is not always, or often, a simple technique. Its aim is always the benefit of the other person, and often the most intricate kind of mental chess playing is required to figure out how to act in a given case with true love. I must always think, "If I do this, what is his reaction likely to be?" Anything that I do for someone, that leaves him feeling indebted to me, is not a perfect act of love. The fact is that being human—"sons of Adam" if you please—we simply are not capable of perfectly loving actions, just as we are not capable of acting without sin. But that is certainly no reason for not doing the best we can at it. I doubt if any scientist would seriously claim that his intellectual honesty was above reproach. With either Christian love or intellectual honesty, wishful thinking is one of the easiest things to stub your toe on. As soon as I say, "But he ought to be pleased if I do such and such for him, and he would be if he weren't such a stinker . . ."—as soon as an idea like this influences me, then I am trying to impose my own ideas and wishes on events. If he is a stinker, then I have got to act in such a way that, being a stinker, he *will* be pleased, or at least really benefited.

There are a number of subsidiary qualities that have been mentioned or implied in the foregoing, which may play a part in the over-all process of Christian love. These include such things as humility, self-sacrifice, the willingness to submit to indignities, etc. But don't confuse these with love itself. Similarly, intellectual honesty makes use of logical thinking, but the two are not identical. The subsidiary qualities that I have just mentioned—humility and so on—may perfectly well be used in other, less Christian ways. A man may be self-sacrificing in the service of his own pride or hatred. Hitler, for instance, was in many ways an ascetic. If someone insults me, and I accept the insult in such a way that he is made to look ridiculous, this is not an act of love, though it may look like humility. In general, conspicuous humility defeats its aims. It may be motivated at the start by Christian ideals, but it can become a particularly devilish form of pride.

5

I'd like to finish up this discussion with a couple of ideas, or hypotheses, of my own. In the first place, I have an idea that it would be perfectly possible for a man to try to act according to the technique that I have been calling Christian love, but from motives that were definitely not Christian. It is conceivable that a wicked man, seeing the results that had been achieved by the world's great figures of love, might decide that, by Satan, he'd try it himself! If he did, and if he really tried to use the technique perfectly, I have an idea that he'd be one of the most surprised men in the world. Because this technique cannot be used to achieve ends other than good. I can't prove this, but I believe experiment would bear me out.

And there is another similar effect in connection with right and wrong. This also can only be verified by experiment, but my own limited experience confirms it. It sometimes happens that we have a good deal of trouble deciding which of two possible courses of action is the better, both being apparently good in themselves. In this case, if we try to find out which is the more loving, it will often settle the question. There are times when this process can cut a Gordian knot that has resisted hours of honest thought.

It is still possible that someone who has gotten this far may ask, "But suppose I do learn this technique, as you call it, and try to apply it. What will it get me?" I suppose I might answer that it will get you power, of a sort. It almost certainly won't get you riches. It probably will enable you to make friends and influence people, but there are much easier ways of doing that. No, I don't think it will get you anything very tangible. It is practically guaranteed to get you headaches, both physical and metaphorical. It is also absolutely guaranteed to get you a kind of satisfaction that comes from no other source.

But Christians tell me that it will get you something of infinitely greater value than anything I have even suggested in what I have said so far. They say that the only reason that we are able to use this technique of love at all is because of God's love for us. This ties in with what

I said in the last chapter, about the reason why God gave us free will. The Christian conception is that he did this in order *that we might be able to love as he loves:* without compulsion and without limit. Naturally there can be no quantitative comparison between our efforts and God's. But precisely insofar as we try to apply this technique in every action of every day in our lives, to just that extent we are approaching the end that God seems to have had in mind when he made us "in his own image."

God so loved the world that he gave his only son to save us from the consequences of our own willful turning away from him. Christ, through his teachings, and finally through his crucifixion, showed us the meaning of perfect love. As fallen man we shall all of us unquestionably continue to sin. But as redeemed man we may, through our own love, freely accept Christ's love for us. We have his assurance that even though we do sin, we can be, and will be, forgiven. And thus we can achieve the salvation that we certainly do not deserve, but that is a free gift, ours if we are merely willing to reach out and take it.

Chapter VII

PAIN

IF THE Christian hypothesis is true, then the world we live in is something different from what it would be if this hypothesis weren't true. Moreover, God himself is seen to be different from what he might be if the hypothesis weren't true.

If we had only our everyday observations and our own logical processes to depend on, then it would be conceivable that the God whose existence can be shown by arguments like the ones given early in this book might be a very impersonal sort of being. He might, for instance, have set the world going according to a definite set of rules, and then gone off and left it to run itself. Or, if he was still interested in it, he might be giving it just enough of his attention to keep it from running all the way into the ditch, while he concentrated primarily on his great universal thoughts. He might even be interested in the human race as a composite entity, but not be particularly interested in the individuals that make it up, just as a chemist who is interested in casein may not care, or even know, just what its composition is in terms of electrons and protons and other elementary particles.

Some such conception of God is indicated here and there all through the Old Testament. We get the impression in a good many places there that God thinks in terms of families, rather than of individuals. For example, a king will do something that angers God, but because of something pleasing that the king has done, God decides not to punish the man himself, but to take it out on his children and grandchildren instead. These poor unfortunates then die miserable deaths, not on account of anything they themselves have done, but for the sins of their ancestor. The same kind of conception seems to lie behind the whole great plan of the Old Testament, where the Jewish people, as a group, have a destiny that God has planned for them. While they are fulfilling this destiny, it doesn't seem to matter to God that thousands or millions of harmless or potentially good people are wiped out, so long as the great central plan is carried through.

It is true that here and there, all through the Old Testament, we see prophets who give a different picture, who suggest that God is not this awful impersonal force, but is always at hand to help any individual who will accept help. From time to time we see the tender picture of God as a shepherd who cares, not only for the flock as a whole, but for each wandering lamb.

When Jesus Christ was born, as a little Jewish baby, into an undistinguished family of Nazareth, there was born at the same time a new conception of what God is. According to the Christian hypothesis, this event was the incarnation of God himself as a human being who was essentially like the rest of the people on earth.

Theologians emphasize the mystery in this incarnation. When you start to look into the complications and the subtleties that are involved, there is almost no limit to the number of logical and rational problems that you run into. The situation is full of paradoxes, and the careful study of these is very important—too important to be more than indicated here. But the fundamental fact of the case is relatively simple. Every human body is inhabited and controlled by a spirit. There is nothing inconceivable at the primary level in the idea that the spirit that inhabited the body of this one human was God's spirit. Let's consider some of the obvious consequences of this momentous event.

In the first place, the Incarnation means that God knows humanity not only in the way a sculptor knows a statue that he has made, or as a novelist knows a character in his book; but that he knows us as a hod carrier knows hod carriers, or as a banker knows bankers. He has been here. Not only that, but as a result of the life that he lived, and the manner of his death, he knows at first hand a great many of the unpleasant things that can happen to us humans.

We can no longer think of him as regarding us merely as a group. He himself was here as the person, the individual, Jesus of Nazareth, who had to earn his living if he weren't to starve, who required his six or eight hours of sleep every night, who had to put food into his mouth, chew it, and swallow it. He had enemies who were not only trying to kill him, but who were trying to discredit the things that he came to teach. And finally he went through the awful experience of seeing these enemies completely triumphant—an experience perhaps worse than the physical torture that they inflicted on him. If his last words on the cross have the implication that we can't help seeing in them, God, as Christ, finally faced the worst thing that can happen to any man; he felt that he was forsaken even by the God in whom he had the most perfect trust and confidence.

Granted that there are paradoxes that are hard to rationalize in some of the things I've just said, culminating in the ultimate paradox of God feeling himself forsaken by God. Yet we do seem to be faced with the historical fact that they happened. Many of the paradoxes can be made acceptable if they are studied with a good will and an open mind.[1]

[1] These paradoxes are considered very carefully, and very honestly, by Dr. D. H. Baillie in his book *God was in Christ*. I recommend it strongly if you want to see how present-day theologians are dealing with matters of this sort.

The important thing is that if all this did happen, then God is not the frightening being that glares out at us from so many pages of the Old Testament. It is true that he is interested in us as the great mass of inhabitants of this earth that he made—he cares about us as races and families—but he also knows us, and cares about us, and loves us, as individuals.

This is the lesson that Christ was continually trying to get across to the people who would listen to him, and it is the lesson that he told so well with his whole life. The four Gospels are crowded with the teaching of it: little one-sentence metaphors, and longer stories that we call parables, and simple rules and commandments. Again and again we hear him speak of God as a father, who would of course not give his son a stone if he asked for bread. He compares God to a shepherd who will leave his whole flock, that is safe for the moment, to hunt up one lost baby lamb.

This is certainly not the God who would punish the seven grandsons of Saul for Saul's treachery toward the Gibeonites. It is not the God who would strike a man dead for touching the sacred ark, when it was in danger of falling off an oxcart. If Christ really lived, then the God of this kind of story is a horrible fantasy of the imagination of a primitive people—a people who had gained some conception of God's power, but who had been unable, most of them, to see any further than this.

2

The God who was shown to us in and by Christ—
the father of all of us, and the fellow worker with all
of us—can't be a God who set the world running, and
then went on to more important business. But if this is
true, then the world itself may not be what it looks like
at first. I have already gone into the "sacramental" nature
of the world, in a general way. Here we'll take up one
specific phase of this.

The world we live in does not seem to be a place made
especially to provide man with a pleasant life. In the first
place, man inhabits a piece of the universe so small that
it is completely negligible in any mathematical account
of the whole. And in the second place, even this infini-
tesimal portion is not gentle to man. As long as there are
floods, droughts, earthquakes and hurricanes, it doesn't
look as though our earth was put here for our immediate
and special convenience.

Not only that, but man himself seems to have been
made in such a way that he can be inhuman (as we ap-
propriately call it) to other men. If this inhumanity
affected only the wicked people themselves, there would
be no particular problem. For as long as free will means
anything, it must imply the freedom for self-destruction.
But when free will means that evil men can inflict pain
of all sorts on men who are *not* evil, then we have a
problem that has got to be solved.

This problem of pain and evil is one that has always bothered honest thinkers, and it is unquestionably one that tends to hold back a good many people who think that otherwise the Christian hypothesis might be acceptable. Just because it is such a universal problem it has been attacked by people of all degrees of competence, and sometimes the least competent have been the noisiest. So a scientist, for instance, who honestly wants to find out what Christianity would do with the hard facts of an unpleasant world, may find that he is given a pair of rosy glasses, and told that his eyes have been deceiving him and all this isn't nearly as bad as it looks.

But there have been plenty of Christian thinkers who have realized that the world *is* as bad as it looks, if not worse, and who have still been able to square this fact with a merciful and loving God. There is no general agreement, even among these, as to details. There is almost unanimous agreement that there is a great deal that we don't know. Consequently there is plenty of room for speculation.

We have to explain the fact that suffering seems to be the rule in this world. Everybody must endure a certain amount of it, and the majority of the people on earth live most of their lives in, or just on the edge of, disease and starvation. But if we accept the Christian hypothesis, then over against the terrible reality of the problem we have another reality that we can count on in our solution.

This is that God not only knows that these evils exist, but has been here and seen, heard and felt them. There is absolutely no possibility that pain was a mistake of God's—something that he didn't really know about. He himself has been whipped with leather thongs, and has had nails driven through his wrists. There is no chance that the suffering that bad men inflict on good men is something that was underestimated when the world was designed, because God himself has seen and felt the suffering. God cannot be like the general who accepts the loss of 10 per cent of his troops in order that the other 90 per cent can gain their objective—because God himself has been one of the lost 10 per cent.

So any Christian attempt to explain pain can start with complete assurance that God knows exactly what it is all about, whether or not we can ever get a truly clear view of it from where we stand.

A second piece of assurance to build our answer on is that if the Christian hypothesis is true, life on this earth is not the ultimate aim of existence. It is true that we don't know even in a vague way what the life to follow this one is to be like. Christ himself said very little about it except in terms that were clearly metaphorical, as when he talked about people sitting at his right hand in the Kingdom of God. But we do know that life here is only one part of a whole. And while this present part is limited by birth and death, what is to come doesn't need to have any end.

3

For convenience I'm going to use the word *pain* in a broad sense from now on. It will mean any kind of discomfort, from what you feel when you step on a tack, through how you feel if you haven't had anything to eat for three days, and on to such sensations and emotions as the ones that may come with the death of a son or a husband.

I'd like to start with a hypothesis. This is that pain, in the natural order of things, is *always* a means of protection; and specifically, that it is a means by which the lower parts of an organism protect themselves against the higher parts. For the purposes of this discussion, something that merely lives is "lower" than something that lives and feels. Above these in order would come wanting, willing, thinking, imagining, and finally, as the highest, loving in the Christian sense.

I once saw a barn burn down. After the fire there was some delicious roast corn where the corn crib had been. The pigs hadn't been harmed by the fire, and they wanted that corn. But the corn was still smoking hot, and even had glowing embers on it in some places. The pigs would work their way up to the pile and try to grab an ear, but again and again they would be burned, and back off squealing. The pain that the fire was causing them was a protection against the harm that would have been done if they had gotten further in among the hot embers. What was driving them back to the fire again and again was their desire to eat that delicious roast corn, and without the pain it might have killed them.

I have chosen this example because we don't need to worry here about notions of spirit, higher impulses of the soul, and so on. We'll come to those later. In the case of pigs, the "lower" that was being protected was simply the living organism of each pig, which was threatened with destruction, and the "higher" was the emotional or sensual drive toward the good food. There was no question of the organism needing this particular food for survival. There was plenty of normal pig food available elsewhere. The pain succeeded in turning the pigs, with their mild hunger, away from the dangerous food, and toward a safer source of supply.

Now let's go down the evolutionary scale a little way, and consider an earthworm. Naturally we can't know exactly how an earthworm feels pain, if it does at all. But we may safely say that it practically does not. It will react violently to certain stimuli, but the reaction stops as soon as the stimulus is withdrawn. Using a somewhat teleological way of expressing it, may we not say that the earthworm scarcely *needs* pain? If the worm gets too near a fire, there is a reflex that makes it turn away. It is unlikely that the worm will keep trying to get too close to the fire in pursuit of some higher end; consequently the reflex action is all that is necessary to protect the worm.

Now this same kind of reflex is present in both the pig and me. If either the pig or I get too close to a fire there will be strong contractions of our muscles which will tend to pull us away. But the pig can disregard those reflexes, and when he does it is only the pain that prevents him from injuring or destroying himself. And if I were trying to save an expensive book that had fallen into the fire I could disregard, not only the reflexes, but even the pain itself, and submit to the injury for the sake of an end that seemed important to me.

It is interesting that in the human organism—which is the one that we know most about from the standpoint of pain—there is wide variation in the amount of pain that different structures feel. It is actually not very uncomfortable to have an operation on your intestines under local anesthesia only. The anesthetic is used only on the surface tissues—the skin and the layer just below it. As soon as the surgeon gets below the wall of the abdomen he can handle, cut and sew the internal organs with very little pain for the patient. I am told that the same thing is true with brain operations, which are often done under local anesthesia. These operations are far from pleasant for the patient, but *pain* from the cutting or mishandling of brain tissue is not an important source of discomfort. And again, there is no *need* that these internal structures should feel pain. It is practically impossible for us to subject these tissues directly to destructive forces while we try to achieve our desires for what we think are higher goods. To reach the deep tissues we must first get through the surface, which is well protected by its pain nerves.

These internal organs have other forms of discomfort which do protect them. You may get a very unpleasant stomach-ache if you eat spoiled creampuffs. Hunger and thirst are discomforts that are hard to localize, but they protect your organism against the certain destruction that would follow if you stopped eating and drinking.

Without going beyond observable facts, then, it seems reasonable to suggest that pain exists naturally in rather direct correlation with will. Where will is negligible, as in an earthworm or an oyster, the organism will react automatically and inevitably in response to danger warnings, and pain presumably is at a minimum. Where will is important, as in the case of an adult human, pain will have to act again and again, as the will forces the organism into situations that threaten to destroy it.

Sorrow is a form of pain that affects humans. We simply don't know whether or not it affects animals, so the consideration of it here must start at the human level. But here, as with physical pain, the fundamental hypothesis seems to apply: in the natural scheme of things, sorrow is a protection of the lower against the higher. If I lose a good camera, I do not feel physical pain, but

I suffer from a discomfort which is very real. I am sorry I have lost the camera, and that sorrow may have a protective effect against a similar loss in the future. This discomfort is a protection of my joy of ownership against the carelessness which resulted from the fact that other things were, temporarily, more important to me than this particular joy.

That camera is of course a very trivial example of sorrow. To go a little higher in the scale of values we might consider a child whose parents go away for a few days. He will probably feel considerable grief that they have left him, and this will be more painful the more his parents have loved him, and the better they usually look out for him. His grief is a response that is as spontaneous as physical pain, and it is the reaction of his emotional and spiritual organism against the harm that threatens it. The "higher," against which the pain is a defense in this case, might be the independence from these very parents, which will ultimately be necessary for the child.

Such forms of suffering as grief over the loss, temporary or permanent, of somebody you love, are always mixed up with a great many other emotional factors. But so is physical pain. There are a good many kinds of pain that we don't usually even recognize as painful, because of these other factors: a pat on the back from a friend, the tug of a comb on a hair, the stinging of knuckles when we knock on a door. These are recognized, put in their place, and forgotten.

4

And this leads to the next step in thinking about pain in general. We are human, with a will, and with something conveniently called a spirit. So we tend to *use* pain, just as we use everything else that we find in the world around us. The most elementary way in which we can use it is just the way nature intended it to be used. I can spank a kitten who persists in getting too close to the rocker of my chair. This pain has the same effect, but in a lesser degree, as would result if a paw got under the rocker. It will tend to protect the physical organism of the kitten from harm. The same thing applies at the human level. I know of a very painful spanking administered by a very loving parent to a child who tried to jump off the platform of a train that was still moving. In both of these cases nature's tools have been deliberately used to accomplish nature's ends—but to do it less violently than nature would have.

We extend the principle a little further when we spank the kitten for messing in the corner under the kitchen table. In this case we are not doing it to make the kitten safer physically, but to make him more acceptable as a companion. At this point, of course, the question can be raised as to whether a trained domestic animal is better off than an untrained one. Whether the animal is a house pet, or a servant like a sheep dog or a work

horse, the training that is required must always be somewhat painful to be effective. We can reduce this problem
to its lowest terms, and say that if the animal is not
trained, we shall not want it around. It will therefore not
be cared for, and may die. In that case the fundamental
purpose of pain is still being accomplished, though re-
motely. But in addition to this, most people who have
had much to do with animals believe that a well-trained
animal has the appearance of being very much happier,
or more satisfied, than a poorly trained one.

And of course we use pain in this same way when we
train children. Here we can and do use pain at levels
higher than the purely physical. In this century there has
been a reaction against the senseless excesses that used to
be thought necessary. Fortunately we have learned that
it doesn't do any good at all to whip a stupid boy who
can't learn a lesson. But the people who tried to avoid
corporal punishment altogether, especially in the nine-
teen twenties and thirties, found that it simply didn't
work. The children that they trained were unhappy children, by and large. Some of these educators, moreover,
found themselves resorting to such punishments as scorn,
or sarcasm, or coldness. While these don't produce physical trauma, they may actually do a great deal more harm
to a child than would a spanking.

It seems that pain is a necessary part of education, and
of almost any other kind of training either of animals or

of man. As we grow up, the burden of applying this pain is shifted from our teachers to ourselves. If I want to climb Mt. Rainier I've got to go through a rather rugged course of training, which will necessarily involve sore muscles. This soreness is the body's response to my insistence on making it do more than it can. Presently the capacity of the muscles increases, partly as a result of, partly in spite of, the pain, and I can do the climbing which might well have killed me if I had tackled it untrained.

5

So far I have considered pain only in its normal function. Perhaps you might say its good function. It serves as a protective or corrective agent, and serves in this way under conditions where no simpler protection would be effective. Since we are endowed with a will, we may disregard the warnings that pain gives us. This doesn't make it any less painful, but we may balance the pain that is holding us back against the desire that is sending us forward, and decide for ourselves which to obey. This is easily understandable, and applies even among the lower animals, where the desire may be a simple appetite.

This disregard for pain is less easy to explain, but is certainly an observed fact, in the case of a soldier who works his way up a hill to take a machine-gun emplacement. The soldier is subject not only to the pain of a bullet which may actually hit him, but to emotional discomforts which may be even more unpleasant: the fear of the pain of the bullet, the longer-range fear of life as a cripple, and finally the fear of death itself. He has balanced these pains against desires which may be purely abstract: the saving of friends in his own battalion who are endangered by the machine gun, or the protection of his country or his religious faith against their enemies.

I'm shying away for a moment from the heart of the problem—why should God have created a world in which it is possible for a machine-gun nest to be manned by people who want to destroy our friends, or our religion, or our country? Pain that is a protection against our own free will is understandable. Pain that is used for training can be considered as an extension of the same thing. But pain that is inflicted needlessly, that does not act visibly in either of these ways, can't be left out of account. I shall come back to that.

First, though, let's take the question of sickness. Why did God create a world in which a harmless, innocent man can be attacked by a disease that will keep him in misery for weeks? Why is it possible for a child to be born incurably blind? Why is it possible for a woman to suffer for years from cancer, and finally die of it?

First, take the man who goes through several weeks of illness. It is not at all unusual to find this man a great deal more human when he has recovered than he was before he got sick. There are very few people in the world more obnoxious than the fellow who has never been sick a day in his life. When sickness has this humanizing effect we are justified in assuming that it has fulfilled one of the primary purposes of pain. Whatever the direct cause of the sickness, its result has been the training of the invalid. He is a better human for having undergone it—as I am a better human for the spanking I got when I was rude to my father.

You will object, very properly, that this doesn't cover the case of the whining invalid, who becomes less and less human as his sickness progresses. But can't he be compared with the bad boy that won't be turned from his mischief by any number of spankings? In the case of the bad boy we may try other means of correction, and sometimes they are successful. In the case of the whining invalid—every so often something or someone comes along that completely transforms his outlook on life, whereupon all the past suffering suddenly becomes valid and useful.

The assumption is not reasonable, of course, if you don't believe in God. The idea of training implies someone who trains. Christians believe that God cares for each one of us. He loves us in the same way that a father loves his children, but to an extent that no human father can. And just as a father must rather often cause pain in his children, so God puts pain in our way for the same purpose—to make better children of us.

Notice that I have not spoken much about punishment. It is a word that I don't like. It gets tangled up with ideas of vengeance and hatred and anger, as well as with correction and training. It seems unlikely that God sends pains and misfortunes our way as punishments for our past misdeeds, as the old Hebrews thought. If God is the loving father that Christ told us about, then it seems much more likely that the pains we have to undergo in this life are in some real way a training for the job that we have to do in the whole life that lies ahead of us. We know that this can happen when someone is sick for a few days or weeks, and gets well. In that case *if* we are immortal, and *if* our life here on earth is part of our preparation for a fuller life to come, then the problem of incurable illness is no longer an insoluble problem. We can't know the nature of the job that we shall be expected to do, starting the day after we die, but the whole essence of Christianity is that there will be such a job, and that our life here is preparing us to do it. If this life contains much pain, for some of us, that may mean simply that these fortunates are going to be allowed to tackle the higher peaks later.

6

And now I think we can come back to that machine-gun nest. It is not too unreasonable to put the pain inflicted by evil men in the same category with the pain caused by bacteria or storms or accidents. From the point of view of the evil man himself, he is simply using his free will as it best pleases him; the rest of us would say that he was misusing it. But from our point of view, his action takes its place in the world right alongside the other "unnecessary" pains. These haven't the specific functions that belong by right to protective pain. We could lead successful organic lives without disease, whereas we could not live at all if burns and bruises and cuts didn't hurt us. Yet these unnecessary pains may play a very important part in maintaining our spiritual health. Just as we gain in strength of will by overcoming our natural obedience to the orders given us by protective pain, so we seem to gain in strength of spirit if we can overcome our tendency to retreat before the attacks of disease, frustration, discouragement, and so on. Whether these are brought on by "acts of God" like earthquakes, hurricanes, or cancer; or by careless or evil men, as happens with train wrecks, wars, robberies, and so on, they furnish us with grist for our own mills. It is not the diseases, and the accidents, and the failures that determine what we shall become. It is what we do with these things when they meet us.

A false conclusion that I may seem to have been leading up to is that pain is a good thing. If pain is one of the important factors that can train us to greater spiritual excellence which we can use in this world or the next, then pain is a fine thing to have around. Why don't we help other people to achieve higher ends by beating them, starving them, or leaving them to die of disease? A very few thinkers have come to a conclusion something like this, but it is of course a dangerous perversion. If pain were the *only* means toward spiritual strength, then some such conclusion might conceivably be valid. But it isn't. Christian love, which has many facets, and includes many ways of giving to other people, is a positive force. In relation to it pain is a kind of negative. Love too can correct, love can train. Pain is a force that tends to beat down the strength of the spirit, and the spirit that can overcome this becomes stronger. But love is a force that acts only upward. It can never destroy. Pain, misused, can do great harm, to spirit as well as to body.

The situation is not as paradoxical as it may seem. Why should we not accept pain, in all its forms, as one of the many things that make up our environment while we live on this earth? Trees, water, food, houses, and even money are not in themselves either good or bad. They are the materials that are given to us to work with on our passage through life. Likewise a stubbed toe and a burnt finger, a boil or a cancer or a robber's bullet— all these things are in themselves neither good nor bad. Since they are unpleasant, we shall do well to avoid them when we can, and to help other people to avoid them. As a matter of fact, I avoid turnips and pumpkin pie, though I know that turnips are nutritious food, and some people think that pumpkin pie is a delicacy.

When pain is unavoidable—when it is either thrust on me without my willing either way, as would be the case with cancer; or when I must meet it in order to accomplish something which I think is important, as would happen if I were attacking that machine-gun nest —then it can be either bad, if I turn my back and run, or it can be very good indeed, if I meet it, and use it to train myself for something further ahead.

7

We still have to take up what is perhaps the most important case of pain in the history of the world. It is what some Christians call the Passion of Our Lord. Surely his pain was not necessary to make a better spirit of him! His training was complete before the world began, because he is the goal of all training.

But remember that the fundamental purpose of pain is to protect a lower portion of an organism against its own higher portion. We wouldn't be shocked to realize that when Jesus was a little boy it hurt him when he stepped on a sharp stone. He had a physical body, and this body had to feel pain if it was to survive. But he also had all the rest of the equipment that goes with being human, including emotions, intelligence and an ego. Each of these, in all of us, is subject to its own kind of pain, which tends to protect it against violation by the spirit. At his trial and on the cross, Christ was consciously sacrificing everything human in him to the demands of his divine spirit. And everything human in him responded by fighting the sacrifice with the weapons that are the normal and necessary protection of each of us throughout life. The last cry on the cross, "My God, why have you forsaken me?"—is the cry of the human ego in its last extremity.

No, that spirit did not need to suffer in order to achieve higher things. And yet even here pain was functioning as a kind of training. If the story of the Resurrection is true, Christ still had a kind of physical body after he died. But this body could no longer feel pain, or hunger, or sorrow. It had become a body which was completely subservient to the orders of the spirit, rather than one that needed to protect its integrity against that spirit. It was, or is, a body perfectly trained to implement a perfect spirit.

But in another sense the suffering of Christ on the cross is the one instance of pain in the universe that needs no explanation, because it is itself the basis of the whole explanation of pain. This suffering is the only thing that makes pain understandable to us humans. If he had not suffered, then no human suffering could be explained. Reasoning back from this you can arrive at the dogmatic statement, that you have often heard, that Christ suffered in order that men might live. His suffering, taken together with the other tenets of the Christian hypothesis, shows that pain is an essential part of life on this earth, not an accidental part. And his love shows how this pain, as well as all the other things that we meet here, can be used to help us live the kind of lives, here and now, that God meant us to live.

Chapter VIII

PRAYER

WHEREVER there is religion, there is prayer. Prayer includes the terrified gabble of an aboriginal savage afraid of an earthquake, the magic rites of a semicivilized Haitian, the ceremony of a Christian church, and the mystical contemplation of a saint. While the basic meaning of the word involves asking or begging for something, all the more advanced religions have extended this meaning to cover any kind of communication with God. Christian prayer, for instance, may include praise, thanksgiving, and confession of unworthiness, as well as requests for benefits for ourselves or other people.

However, I'm going to limit what we'll take up here to prayer in its original meaning: asking God to give us something, or to do something that we want done. If this aspect of prayer can make sense, there should be no particular difficulty with the rest.

I

Some scientific explanations for the efficacy of prayer are a good deal like the scientific explanations of miracles. They may be true in a limited way, but they tend to leave out the important facts. For instance, a good many psychologists now admit that prayer is very valuable. They may explain this on the basis that when you pray, particularly if it is strength and guidance you are asking for, you concentrate on your problems. This concentration then helps you to solve the problems. An explanation like this makes sense, as far as it goes. But if it stops there, you might just as well pray to a beetle, or to your dead great-grandfather, as to God. If prayer is to have any meaning for a Christian, it must consist of real requests, which are addressed to a God who is real, with the expectation that he hears them and will in some way answer them.

There are explanations that try to bring in recent discoveries in the field of extrasensory perception, and imply that all the results of prayer are merely the result of thought-transference. Again, this is not a Christian explanation. It explains the result by a denial of the fact of God, rather than by a recognition of it. It seems to me quite possible that there is a connection between thought-transference and the phenomenon of group-will that I'm going to talk about a little later. But the basic phenomenon in this case has been known much longer than the so-called explanation. It must be admitted that we still know much too little about extrasensory perception to be able to use it with any confidence as an explanation for anything else.

So I'm going to see what I can do with the facts and hypotheses that have already been discussed, plus a little new material that seems to be admissible. Any explanation of mine will of course be incomplete, but I'll try to see that it is at least somewhat Christian.

As I see it, one of the strongest objections to prayer may come, not from the side of science, but from a superficial understanding of religion itself. If God knows what we need before we ask him, and if he is our loving Father —and both of these things are true according to the Christian hypothesis—then why in the world should we even have to do the asking? Christ himself has said that God knows what we need before we ask for it. The implication seems to be that prayer is unnecessary. Yet Christ prayed a great deal, and specific requests were prominent in such of his prayers as were reported. The form of prayer that he recommended for all of us contains a series of important requests: for food, for mercy, for freedom from trials and dangers.

But this paradox can be straightened out if we look a little more carefully at what we are given to work with. God knows what is best for us, it is true, and he'd like to have it happen to us. Yet since he has made us what we are, he can't make these good things happen to us unless we want them.

And the key to this is in those last four words—unless we want them. Our fundamental thesis assumes that we were given free will. If this is true, then of *his* free will God has decided not to exercise certain of his powers, and particularly his power to compel us to do what would be best for us. This is not to say that God in his omnipotence *cannot* compel us, but that he will not. If he did, then the concept of love, which is the deep foundation of Christianity, would be meaningless. We are free at every moment to act out of love toward God, or to act according to our own immediate self-love. That is, we may do what we believe God wants us to do, or we may follow the promptings of our present desires and appetites. If we don't have this freedom, then nothing that we do would have any more significance than the moves that a pawn makes on a chess board.

It is interesting that philosophies that try to deny free will, and make us mere tools in God's hand, quickly contradict themselves. If I am not free, then I might as well follow every impulse that occurs to me, since everything I do is what God intended me to do. This leads immediately to depravity, which is absurd if I am a tool in the hand of a good and loving God.

God does know, then, what is best for me, but he

won't make it happen to me unless I want it to happen. And thus my prayers are just as definitely acts of will as are any other actions of my life. If I decide not to pray— not to ask God for anything—that is up to me. But it is entirely comparable to a decision to build a house without the help of any architects or carpenters or plumbers. I may get the house built, but it probably won't be very handy as a place to live.

If I leave out prayer deliberately, after careful consideration of all the factors that are involved, it means that I intend to live my life isolated from God's will. If I could follow that policy to its logical conclusion I should be trying to imitate a famous though unhappy predecessor, who has been called by various names, such as Satan, and Lucifer. I probably wouldn't make it though, on account of another kind of prayer that we're going to take up in a minute.

But if I decide that I do want to do what God would like me to, then prayer makes very good sense. Every time I ask God to help me in some way, I am at the same time giving him permission to help me. He simply cannot do this unless I ask for it. If he did, he would be violating the very freedom he has given me.

If in my prayer I really ask God to do what is best for me, then obviously I ought not to be very much surprised if he doesn't give me exactly what I have asked for. Christ said that God won't give me a stone if I ask for a piece of bread. But likewise, if I stupidly ask for a stone to satisfy my hunger, I ought not to be disappointed if he gives me beefsteak instead.

Experimental evidence on the effectiveness of prayer is hard to evaluate, since most people who do pray are frankly biased before they start. Yet, even taking this into account, it seems proper to accept the fact that prayers are answered surprisingly often, in about the way they are asked. People who pray a great deal, and who believe firmly in the fatherliness of God, tell us with every evidence of honesty that prayers make a great deal of difference in the ordinary happenings of everyday life.

A conventional objection to the assumption that prayer can affect the nonhuman world around us has been that this implies God changing his mind in answer to our requests. The answer to this objection has already been suggested in an earlier chapter: there is no need for God to rearrange the universe in answer to our prayer, since he knew about the prayer when the universe was first being arranged. And it follows further from this that the better we make our own aims coincide with his aims, the more literally our prayers are likely to be fulfilled. The most extreme case of this sort of thing is of course the traditional miracle, where God has stepped in at our request, and applied laws that we didn't even know existed, because he approved so highly of what we were trying to do.

2

There is another kind of request that I can make of God, which is decidedly different from what we have just been considering. This is called intercession. It consists of asking God to help somebody else. What we have dealt with so far is prayers for help for me, the person who is doing the praying. Praying for somebody else is more loving, and therefore should be a more Christian action than praying for myself. Yet here the objection that we have just been trying to meet becomes even more serious. If God is unable to help me unless I ask for his help, how can I expect him to help my friend? We have just seen that he can't give help where it isn't wanted.

Take a specific case. A friend of mine is sick, and I ask God to help him. It is possible, first of all, that this prayer may fall into the class we have just been talking about. A good many people seem to be able to make sick people better simply by being in the room with them. Some people have this power to such a degree that they have become world-famous. In asking for the healing of my friend, I may be asking for some of this particular power for myself. If it suits God's purpose the prayer may be answered, since it is just like any other prayer that concerns me.

But there is a second aspect to this prayer. If I really

mean it, I am not just asking God to make my friend well. We have seen that pain and sickness may be an important part of the friend's spiritual training, and it is possible that it might be bad for him to get well right now. So my prayer must include the request that he be given the grace and the good sense to make the best use of his sickness, even if he doesn't get well. And in this case it looks as though I am asking God to do for my friend what he can't do for me—step in and interfere with a free will. And it would seem that this prayer of mine can't be answered, unless the friend can be persuaded to ask for the help himself. Yet Christians do pray for their friends, and even for their enemies who almost certainly don't want God's help—or don't know that they want it. Why?

Frankly, I don't know. I have heard a great many very intelligent people say that they were sure that this kind of prayer is effective. It has been reported again and again that at the moment when such a prayer was being offered, in a distant spot, the sick person became better, or more peaceful. If this effect is a fact, then it must fit into the Christian framework. And I can guess how it fits.

We do not live alone in the world. We are members of groups: families, schools, cities, nations, and so on. And there is a growing realization that these groups, large or small, have certain characteristics that are not explainable entirely in terms of the individuals that make them up.

This fact has been known for a long time in connection with the particular form of nastiness called mob psychology. Men who have been caught in a mob know that it does strange things to the will. A man who is normally a pretty good fellow, and who would never deliberately go out to hurt somebody else, may find when he gets caught in a lynch mob that he does things willingly for which he has no good explanation later. His will has become subordinated to the will of the mob. The same thing is true of all the other men making up that mob. No one of them, individually, is responsible for what the group does. But the unit, consisting of all of them, has willed it, and is responsible for it.

I have mentioned this unpleasant case first because it is perhaps the best-known example of group-will. But crowd psychology doesn't have to be bad. A crowd at a football game may go wild, but in a thoroughly good-humored way. And you may get a crowd at an auction, who see that a small boy wants a particular item that is up for sale, and who act as a unit in refusing to make an opposing bid.

In the cases I have mentioned there is no question of the will of the individual being completely taken over by the will of the group. People in lynch mobs can refuse to agree with the mob's actions; but it is generally agreed that this refusal takes a good deal more strength of will than would the same refusal without the mob. And of course it takes a very strong man indeed to stand up and face the mob, but in this case many other factors come into the picture.

The fact that people act as groups as well as individually has been recognized, in Christian tradition, through the concept of the "Mystical Body of Christ." The phrase symbolizes something that Christians seem to have been aware of since very soon after the Resurrection: that each of us is a part of a unit which is very much greater than himself. St. Paul gives a picture of this idea when he compares Christians of different occupations to different parts of one body. They may be doctors, lawyers, laborers, ministers, just as a body has a head, arms, legs, a heart and so on. And just as all the parts of a single physical body work together for the good of the whole, so the proper functioning of each member of the "mystical" body is necessary for the welfare of this greater unit, which includes all Christians, or perhaps all men of good will.

This hypothesis seems to be consonant with good modern psychology. If it is, we have a perfectly acceptable explanation for the value and effectiveness of intercessory prayer. It is true, as I said, that God can't help my friend unless the friend is willing to accept the help. But this willingness can itself be brought about without the *direct* activity of my friend's will. Since he and I are members of the one group (whether you call it a mystical body, or just a group of friends) any action of my will affects his will to some extent. And if a group of people, either together in one place, or even separately, are praying for him, there is every reason why his will should be moved in the direction that the rest of us want it to be. He may of course oppose us. He may refuse our help, and thereby God's help. But this has to be a deliberate refusal if it is to be effective.

3

And now I can tie in a thought that I left dangling several pages back. This is that if I try to make *my* will be done, rather than God's, I'll be following in the footsteps of the devil. And this brings up the question of eternal damnation. Is it possible that the God who is our loving Father could actually condemn any soul to eternal torment?

First, let me point out that very few enlightened Christians think that God simply gets angry at someone and tells him to go to hell. Whatever damnation is, it is something to which we condemn ourselves. We can resolutely refuse to accept the gifts that God is always holding out to us. But if we do, it is not he who is turning his face away from us; it is we who turn our backs on him. So if anyone goes to hell, it is because he doesn't want to go to heaven.[1]

[1] Since nobody knows anything about what hell is like, it has been a favorite field for the exercise of vivid imaginations. A contemporary example of this is C. S. Lewis' very short book, *The Great Divorce*.

But *eternal* damnation, the cutting off of a soul from any possibility of *ever* becoming reconciled to God, simply doesn't make sense. It just doesn't fit with the rest of Christianity.

We have seen that at every step I take I can decide whether that step is to take me nearer to God or farther away from him. If I were alone in the universe, then it is barely conceivable that in spite of all God's own direct and indirect persuasion I might always decide against him. Even this, as soon as it is stated, sounds a little absurd. But this situation is a purely hypothetical one. I am *not* alone. I am a human, surrounded by other humans. Among these there will always be some who love me. Take the extreme case of an unwanted child born of a prostitute mother and a drunken father, and brought up in a world where cruelty and vice are the rule. Even so, we know that there are always men who give their lives to just these hopeless cases. Such men follow the example of St. Francis of Assisi, who recognized *all* men as his beloved brothers. If intercessory prayer is valid, then as long as there is a saint left in the world, the eternal damnation of a sinner is impossible.

On the other hand, a doctrine that permits me to make my ultimate salvation as difficult as possible, *short* of eternal damnation, would seem to be in complete accord with the Christian hypothesis. In the long run, and with the help of his loving children, God's will is going to be done. But in the short run, as long as God has made free will a part of the scheme of things, I can make it necessary for God's will to go all around Robin Hood's barn if I insist. If your six-year-old, due for a bath tonight, runs away and kicks and screams and bites, it may take you quite a while to give him that bath. But he'll get it in the end, and in the course of the evening he will acquire considerably more training than was originally implied in the idea of the bath. If God is loving, he wants every soul to be saved; therefore every soul will be saved. Our misdirected free will can put off that salvation almost indefinitely, if we try hard enough. But I can't believe that we can put it off forever.

4

Many Christians believe in the existence of the devil as a spiritual entity: a person just as real as you or I. In the past it has been taught that the devil is doomed to suffer torments in hell forever. He is the classic case of a soul who decided that his own will was the most important thing in the world. He is supposed to have opposed this will of his to God's. In the test of strength God won, not surprisingly, and the devil was kicked out of heaven. He is sometimes supposed to have been one of the highest of the angels before his fall, and it is acknowledged that he still has tremendous powers for good. In fact, it is precisely the corruption of these powers that makes him so bad. For instance, he is exceedingly wise, and wisdom is a very good thing. He is presumably beautiful. He has a kind of nobility—has the reputation of keeping his bargains. But he is very proud, and pride is the complete antithesis of everything that a Christian means by love.

Every so often somebody, thinking about the problem of evil, happens to be struck by the sadness of the devil's position. And such a person may offer up a little prayer to God, asking him to have mercy on the devil himself.

God, as we get the picture, wants to have mercy, but the devil won't accept it. Yet each time the prayer is offered, the will of the group (the group of all spirits, of which even the devil is a member) makes a new little attack on the devil's isolation. Who can say, given unlimited time, that God may not eventually be welcomed back into the last soul in the world that has tried to shut him out?

5

Psychologists may explain prayer as being merely an effective form of concentration. On the basis of what we have now gone over, it seems to me that this is no explanation of Christian prayer. If you want to pray in a way that will be psychologically effective, you have to try to convince yourself that you must have what you are asking for, and that you are capable of achieving it. A very real faith must be built up; faith in yourself and your own abilities. The success of the fad of Dr. Coué, back in the twenties, showed how effective this method could be. People used to repeat, again and again, the little sentence, "Every day, in every way, I'm getting better and better."—And they *did* get better and better. People with all kinds of troubles and diseases got over them, there's no question about it.

If this kind of thing had anything to do with Christian prayer, then the explanation would be acceptable. Of course some Christians do pray this way all the time, and practically all of them do occasionally. But as Christ taught us to pray, both in the Lord's Prayer, and in his other prayers that have been quoted, the form is entirely different from the psychologically effective one. He taught us to say, not "God, please give me this because I want it and should have it," but "God, please let me have this if it is right; but if it isn't, then thy will be done." And the last half of that is very bad psychology.

Notice that both psychological prayer and Christian prayer require faith. But in the first it is faith in myself, and that I shall get what I want, whereas in the second it is faith in God, and that I'll get what God knows is best for me—possibly something entirely different from what I think I want.

Come back again to the question, "If your son asks you for bread, will you give him a stone?" If I pray in what should be a psychologically effective way, I'll get stones for breakfast if I want them enough. But if I am a Christian, and stupid enough to pray for stones for breakfast, I'm more likely to get buttered toast—if buttered toast is what God knows I need.

The difference between the two kinds of prayer points up even more clearly the difference between the Christian and the atheistic or humanistic approach to life. The Christian approach appeals to God, with a willingness to admit that I myself—consciously or subconsciously—am not the best judge of my needs, and am not best able to satisfy them. The other approach is a falling back on my own resources alone, and can result, in extreme cases, in a retreat from the realities of the world around me, into my own self-sufficient isolation.

I have seen it stated that petitionary prayer is a "low" form of spiritual activity, as compared with the petitionless communion of the great saints and mystics. This is a reasonable view if the petitions are handled in the psychologically effective way. But if the aim of the requests is the fulfillment of God's will, it is certainly not less acceptable for me to ask for his help in making the best use of my own free will than it would be for me to suspend that free will altogether in mystical contemplation of the Infinite Goodness.

At the same time, let me make it clear that the contemplative kind of prayer, of the mystic, is not the vague and unreasonable kind of thing that "practical" people sometimes think it is. When a man withdraws from the world for a time, or even permanently, and devotes himself entirely to prayer, he is not necessarily retreating from reality. He may be doing what he believes to be the most practical thing he can do to bring about the accomplishment of God's will.

The mystical approach may actually be much more understandable to scientists than to people in other occupations. A great many scientists are working on problems that seem to the rest of the world to have only the faintest connection with practical affairs. These scientists may talk, for publication, about the possibility that some practical use may yet be made of their results—and this unquestionably does happen in surprising ways once in a while. But a tremendous amount of the creative work done by scientists now and in the past is simply buried in the archives—in a sense lost. We all know this, but it doesn't keep us from working at our problems, practical or impractical.

The mystic and the physicist, for instance, are much closer together today than people fifty years ago could have dreamed. Both of them are engaged in attempts to get in touch with the ultimate reality of things, and both of them find that the further they go, the harder it is for them to express their discoveries in terms that make sense to a layman. Yet each is sure that his work has real significance.

As long as prayer consists of demands—demands made to myself, or to an imagined shopping service in the sky —it can certainly be considered as a low form of spiritual activity. But as soon as it rises above this level, and begins to be an attempt to make my desires coincide with the aims of God, then there can be no further gradation into "low" and "high" forms of prayer. Every mystic must spend much of his time in petition, and each mere petitioner is trying to reach communion with God.

Chapter IX

FAITH

THERE aren't very many of the Christian virtues that I'm really good at. But in contemplating this chapter I have been overwhelmingly aware of one of these virtues—humility. When I have looked at the subject, alongside of my ability to deal with it, the prospect has not been pleasing. But because the problem of faith is the toughest thing that a scientist is likely to meet in Christianity, it is something that I have got to take up.

I

You could hardly invent two more perfect contraries than the traditional scientific attitude, and the traditional conception of faith. The scientist begins with doubt; faith begins with belief.

A scientist can be deprived of his laboratory, his instruments, even his library, and still be able to function effectively as a scientist. These are, in a sense, no more essential to him than are the bacon and eggs he has for

172

breakfast. He may be able to work better if he has them, but he should be able to change his tools as easily as his diet if this is necessary or desirable. On the other hand, if he loses either his ability to doubt, or his honesty in considering his results, he loses his identity as a scientist. He may still work in a laboratory; he may still weigh, measure and observe; but the salt will have lost its savor.

Against this we have the traditional idea of faith as a willingness to believe anything contained in "the revealed truth," and to deny anything contrary to it. St. Thomas Aquinas, for instance, concludes some arguments with the sentence, "But this is contrary to the Faith (*contra fidem*) and therefore impossible." That *contra fidem* has the same validity in medieval argument as "contrary to the evidence" has in contemporary science. "The Faith" had the standing of an absolute fact. It was something that God himself had established; and God cannot lie. It was like the axioms of Euclid: self-evident; not provable, but not needing proof.

I have called this the *traditional* idea of faith. Yet actually it has been more complicated than this for a long time. With the Crusades, the wandering friars, the spread of education across Europe, and finally the invention of the printing press, "The Faith" as an absolute began to change. What one monk preached one week might differ perceptibly from what another one had said the week before. Ideas brought back from the Holy Land might not exactly coincide with domestic truth. And when the Bible became readily available to everybody, each reader might have his own ideas about the interpretation of a given passage, or might worry as to whether accepted practice was in accordance with the written word of God.

With the Renaissance, and the Reformation, men began more and more to look into truth as it appeared to their own eyes, instead of having to look through approved eyes of the past. Here and there evidence began to show up which seemed to indicate that the so-called word of God might itself be a mistaken word in places. The Church tried to fight ideas of this sort, but it was a losing battle. Gradually truth as we discover it for ourselves had to be admitted to an equal footing with truth as it is revealed to us by specially authorized sources.

Nowadays, except in a very few of the more extreme sects, a Christian is no longer required to believe everything he reads in the Bible. Once the historians started applying to religious history the methods which had been so effective on the secular side, this was inevitable. The Bible, apart from being in some way "inspired," also purports to be history. As such, it is certainly open to critical investigation. We have already taken up one or two aspects of the New Testament from this point of view, and a good deal of it seems to stack up pretty well. But when you go back of that, into the Old Testament, there is more trouble. A great deal of it is still great literature. There is still a lot of good history there. But when we find that some of the "prophecies," which used to be used to prove the authenticity of the whole, may have been written *after* the events they were fore-telling, many of the old arguments lose their force. The contemporary Christian feels entirely justified in looking at any of the statements in the Bible as evidence to be evaluated, rather than as axioms to be accepted.

To this extent then the old idea of faith has vanished or is fading quickly. We may still talk about the Bible as the word of God, but when we do, we mean something different from what we used to. We may still think that God really talked to Moses, and to St. John the Evangelist. But we are now pretty sure that what got written down was not a verbatim transcript of the conversation, but Moses', or John's ideas of what was said; or even other men's ideas about their ideas.

2

Then what is left of Christian faith?

Frankly, I find that Christians, including those who apparently have this faith to a very high degree, are unable to explain just what it is that they have. They do have a very real feeling of knowing the truth, or a piece of the truth. The evidence that is presented to them by history, Biblical or otherwise, and by their own empirical findings in connection with such things as prayer and the partaking of the sacraments, is so convincing that they no longer have any doubt at all that certain things are true.

Since it is so hard to explain faith, people usually try to do it by means of analogies. In my search for what faith means I have had ones like the following presented to me. A man has a perfectly happy family life. Then, when he comes home in the evening we can easily conceive of his having perfect faith that his family still loves him. Or: I have known Jones for a long time, and I have perfect faith that he is telling the truth, on a given occasion, insofar as he knows it. Or: during the twenty years that I have been married, and exceedingly happily married, I have seen no evidence of infidelity on the part of my wife; I can certainly say that I have complete faith that she has not got a secret lover.

Now analogies are perfectly good things to use to illustrate something, or to explain something that is rather subtle. God knows I have used enough of them in the course of this book. But all of these analogies for faith seem to miss somewhere. They leave me cold. There are worse ones, to be sure, which have also been thrown at me. I have been told that I have faith that the sun will rise tomorrow. I have been told that at least I know that I exist.

The more aware among my informants admit that the "sun will rise" analogy is not good. There will certainly come a day when the sun will *not* rise. Do I exist? That depends on what we mean by I and by existence. As to the rest, I'm sorry, but a faith analogous to what is described there has no meaning for me. As to my family loving me, or Jones telling the truth, or my wife being faithful . . . I'm sorry, but I don't *know*.

Over against that, though, let me say what I *do* know (first granting, of course, that I don't know anything; but we went over that in the second chapter). I do think that the probability that the sun will rise tomorrow is so great that for all practical purposes I can neglect the alternative (though I shall enjoy thinking about it). I think that the probability that my family loves me is even greater than the probability that the sun will rise tomorrow (but since I don't see why they should, I shall certainly speculate on what would happen if I got what I deserve). And I think that the probability that my wife has a secret lover is so minute that it delights me to speculate about the possible ways in which this *could* be true, despite all the evidence.[1]

If that is faith, and if faith is necessary for salvation, then I'm afraid I can't make it.

3

Therefore, I'd like to close this chapter, and the book, with a very tentative outline of what the word *faith* can

[1] My wife, to whom I have been married happily for twenty years, and without whom I certainly couldn't have written this book, insists on a footnote here. I really don't know what I can say in it, though.

properly mean to me, and perhaps to others who are in a position similar to mine. I hope that I can arrive at something that will be in accord with all the evidence now at my disposal, that will be acceptable to honest and open-minded scientists, and that will perhaps not be too repugnant to my friends among the clergy.

The evidence that I have to work with is, on the surface, paradoxical. It consists of two general types of data. First, faith has almost unlimited power to produce real effects in a real world; it is of the utmost importance in the Christian scheme. But second, the things that have been believed by the faithful have always included certain things that were not true.

Let me expand a little on these points. Ever since the very early part of Christ's ministry there has been the greatest of stress on belief: ". . . so that those who believe in him may not perish, but have eternal life." St. Paul lists as the three most important virtues, Faith, Hope and Love (though he does place love above faith). In another passage, the author of the Epistle to the Hebrews goes at great length into the importance of faith throughout the whole story of the Old Testament, from Abel to the prophets.

This faith has carried with it, first, an inward assurance, which has enabled believers to act with a calm heroism that has astounded even their critics and torturers. But it has also conferred powers that seemed almost superhuman. When Christ said, "If you have faith as a grain of mustard seed . . . nothing will be impossible to you," he was probably not exaggerating. Throughout history, people with the kind of faith he was talking about *have* moved mountains. With this power, backed by the technique of love, they have been almost literally invincible.

But now we come to the unquestionable fact that a good many of the things that the faithful believed have been quite simply untrue. For instance, there are numerous passages, both in the Epistles, and even in the Gospels, making it clear that the members of the early Church believed firmly that the Judgment, and the Second Coming, were just around the corner—would happen during the lifetime of some of them. Later, St. Augustine proved that there could not be people living at the Antipodes (that is, about where Australia is) because all the descendants of Noah were accounted for on *this* side of the world. He didn't deny that there might be lands on the other side of the earth, but they must be without inhabitants. And even in our own time there is a diminishing number of people who really believe that God created the world in six twenty-four-hour days, in about 4004 B.C.

At first glance this looks like an absurd kind of situation. How can a "faith" include, along with inward strength and outward power, actual falsehood? But strangely enough a situation rather closely analogous to this stares us in the face every day of our scientific lives. In an earlier chapter I pointed out that it is possible for a scientist to postulate that there are no such things as laws of nature; that is, that there is no reality underlying the observed behavior of real things. Yet in fact all his work, and even his existence, become impossible if he does seriously accept such a postulate. Every scientist knows that he has only the haziest idea of what these "laws of nature" are. He knows that every statement of them is nothing but an approximation, sometimes better, sometimes worse. Yet by means of these approximations he has been able to . . . move mountains.

When Robert Boyle first announced in 1660 that if you increased the pressure on an enclosed sample of air, its volume would change in inverse ratio to the pressure, he was stating what we now know to be an untruth. It was an approximation; a pretty fair approximation in the case of a few gases. But nowadays no scientist who is familiar with the subject will even try to tell you exactly what the relationship is between the volume of a gas and the pressure on it. And yet no scientist doubts that there is such a relationship, and many of them are spending their lives trying to find more exactly what it is.

Hooke's laws of stress, Newton's laws of motion, have built many a bridge and flown many an airplane; yet these laws are not true. Einstein has made Newton obsolete, and engineers know that the stress-strain relationship is too complicated to be expressed even approximately in a single law.

Analogies are dangerous things. Push them too far and they are liable to blow up in your face. But in this case I think that maybe the analogy is particularly permissible.

What all Christians believe is that there is an absolute truth which underlies the written and spoken doctrines of the Christian religion. This belief is not just analogous to, but is identical with, the scientist's belief (or working hypothesis) that there is an absolute truth underlying the regularities which we think we observe in the behavior of material things.

While recognizing the beauty of the language, non-Christians sometimes tend to forget that the words written in the Bible represent the thoughts of some very wise men. When St. Paul wrote, "Now we see dimly, as though in a mirror, but then we shall see face to face," he was expressing, both clearly and poetically, the thought that I am trying to put into modern scientific jargon. St. Paul, for all his faith (which enabled him to do the most astounding things), had no idea that *he* knew what Christianity meant. He knew just one thing for certain: that he believed in Jesus Christ, who had risen from the dead. He knew that Christ had come to save mankind, and perhaps Paul. Beyond that, anything might be wrong, distorted in the mirror.

And this, I think, explains the apparent paradoxes that

we find in the evidence concerning faith, this faith that has been an empirical fact down through the ages. God (whatever that means) sent (whatever that means) his son (whatever that means) to redeem (whatever that means) mankind (whatever that means). We are told by Christians that if we can believe this, or even if we only believe "in Christ" (whatever *that* means), we shall be assured of eternal life (whatever that means).

4

In the service of confirmation of the Episcopal Church, the last question the bishop asks the confirmands is: "Do you promise to follow Jesus Christ as your Lord and Savior?" And perhaps the whole answer to the question of faith lies in the "I do" that answers this question.

I may conceivably find that I do not believe firmly in the fact of the virgin birth. I may find that I am not sure whether or not a piece of bread and a cup of wine, there on the altar, are actually transformed in some way to become the body and blood of Christ. I may feel that to speak of Christ as the "Son of God" is not the same thing as to speak of him as God Incarnate. I may have very serious doubts about whether any human being has a very clear idea of what the real meaning is of the Incarnation and the Crucifixion.

These are beside the point when we are talking about faith. Christian faith means the willingness to follow, or at any rate to try to follow, in the way marked out for us by Jesus Christ our Lord and Savior. This means that we must do our best to find out just what the way *is* that was marked out for us. The fact that so many earnest Christians belong to so many different denominations shows that there is considerable area for disagreement as to just what Christ meant by some of the things he said, and even some disagreement as to whether he did some of the things he is said to have done.

As I said earlier, scientists claim that they are interested in facts and the things that can be done with them. If so, then it is a scientist's job to see whether the alleged facts of Christian doctrine *are* facts, not to assume that all Christianity is a fake because some Christians believe patent absurdities. And here is where there is opportunity to use every one of the characteristics that go to make up a creative scientist. *Of course* we may doubt. Of course we may ask questions. We may experiment. We must use to the full every bit of intellectual honesty we possess. There is room for serendipity in observing any human action.

But in addition to the tools that our laboratory instructors trained us to use, we now have a whole new set. Christian love is an approach that will solve a good many problems, not only in psychology, economics and politics, but in the oldest field for scientific activity—theology. If Christians are to be believed at all, prayer is a tool that scientists can use as effectively as priests can. It is effective over the whole range of spiritual activity, from the understanding of a problem in automotive engineering, through the construction of a nuclear reactor, to the study of the meaning of atonement.

Throughout this book I have kept, as far as possible, to a hypothetical approach to every theological question that has been considered. This I believe to be essential if our ideas of the truth about God—and therefore of the truth about the world we live in—are to become more and more accurate. But hypotheses are not actions. And as living beings we are continually acting. Every action is in fact based on a faith of some kind. And the one requirement of Christian faith is that we try to *follow* Jesus Christ as our Lord and Savior. However tentative our approach to any action, however great our doubts as to its wisdom or foolishness, a moment comes when we can no longer hypothesize: we must act. And at the moment of action we may properly act in the light of Christian faith, whether we are scientists or politicians, priests or artists, Catholics or Protestants.

The scientific method is a way of approaching truth. Christian faith is a way of acting in the light of the truth as we see it. Christian *doctrine* gives us a whole new set of keys to use in trying to unlock the treasure house of truth. But Christian *faith* simply insists that we use what treasure we have already found, in the attempt to follow along the path that one man once walked perfectly.

There are literally no limits to the possible achievements of the scientific method, broadly interpreted as I have tried to interpret it here. And Christian faith, accompanying it step by step up the ladder of truth, can transform each new triumph of knowledge into triumphant action.

EPILOGUE

THIS book is, for me at least, only a beginning. Even while I have been writing it I have been realizing its inadequacy. And while the statement at the end of the last chapter is a perfectly honest statement of my position at this moment, I know that it falls far short of the kind of faith that is held by really convinced Christians. As I said earlier, I am told (and I think I believe) that there comes a point, for the student of Christianity, at which he changes from merely accepting these facts as very probable truths, to *knowing* that Christ is in some way our Savior. However incompetent we know ourselves to be, Christ is to be trusted if we go the whole way and put our whole trust in him. But for me, right now, this state of affairs must be put in a class with the rest of Christian doctrine. I can accept it too as being very probably true, but not as *certainly* true.

Before I started writing the book I did a certain limited amount of reading, and spent a good deal of time in discussion with other people. I recommend both these courses of action to anybody who has read this far. And I hope that if you follow this advice you will be as fortunate as I was in the people who discuss the subject with you, and who recommend books to read.

I want to express my indebtedness particularly to Father Gabriel Verkamp, of St. Benedict's Church in Evansville, Indiana, who gave me an unconscionable amount of his time and his wisdom; and to Father Walter W. McNeil, Jr. and Canon David R. Cochran of Christ Church in Seattle, for a remarkable series of sermons, as well as for their help and criticism while I was working on the manuscript for this book. I shall not try to name all the others—in fact there are some whose names I don't even know— but if they read the book, I hope they will recognize the thoughts that came from them, and accept my thanks which are expressed in this way.

However, even though she usually prefers to remain anonymous, it is important to mention the lady who was treated so shabbily on page 177. Every idea that has been taken up in the book has been talked, argued and fought over with Carol, my wife. Any lucidity that may occasionally appear is probably due to her, and you can thank her for a great many half-baked thoughts that have been left out.

As to the books that I have used, I can't possibly give proper credit, since I have stolen so much from so many. For their effect on me personally I know that I am most heavily indebted to a number of C. S. Lewis' books, particularly his *Christian Behavior,* and the *Problem of*

Pain. I read Alan Richardson's very valuable *The Gospel and Modern Thought* while I was writing this, and have included a quotation from it (with his very kind permission) at the end of chapter V. I'm now in the middle of *Nature, Man and God,* by William Temple, and only regret that I didn't start it earlier.

Beyond these particular titles, and some that I've mentioned in footnotes, I hesitate to recommend specific books. The literature in modern theology is so wide, and my knowledge of it so narrow, that the best advice I can possibly give you is that you consult with a good theologian, and get him to suggest the books that he thinks will be particularly useful to you.

Where can you find a good theologian? You might start with the church nearest to you, and call on the pastor—whether he calls himself priest, minister or preacher. If he is unable to help you himself, he will certainly turn you over to somebody who can. And I hope you have as much fun with him as I have had so far!

Index

INDEX